NORTH SEA

BAWDSEY MANOR 1943

BAWDSEY — BIRTH OF THE BEAM

Kindest Regards to a Bawdsey Friend

Gordon K.

BAWDSEY — BIRTH OF THE BEAM

The History of R.A.F. Stations Bawdsey and Woodbridge

TERENCE DALTON LIMITED

LAVENHAM   .   SUFFOLK

1983

Published by
TERENCE DALTON LIMITED

ISBN 0 86138 017 7

Text photoset in 11/12pt Baskerville

Printed in Great Britain at
The Lavenham Press Limited, Lavenham, Suffolk

Contents

Acknowledgements

ONCE again very many people and organisations have assisted me by furnishing unique and very valuable information of the greatest interest. All are so worthy of full individual thanks and notes, were space available, but within these limits I would like to record my sincere thanks to the individuals and groups listed here alphabetically.

Mr Joe Allan, Bedworth; Mr Peter Barker, Ipswich; Mr N. R. Bartlett, Danbury; Mr David Barton, Ipswich; Mrs Christina Bayley, Felixstowe; Mrs E. W. Beck, Preston; Mrs Dorothy Bell, Banbury; Mr Chaz Bowyer, Norwich; Mr M. J. F. Bowyer, Cambridge; British Aerospace, Manchester, and Mr H. Holmes; British Aerospace, Hatfield, and Mr M. V. Brown; Mr A. W. Brooks, Bawdsey; Mr J. M. Bruce, R.A.F. Museum, Hendon; Mr Derek Bullingham, Felixstowe; Mr Jack Bushby, Leek; Mr Ron Buxton, Ipswich; Mr C. Chandler, Ipswich; Mr R. A. Cheetham, Leigh; Churchill College, Cambridge, and Miss M. M. Stewart; Miss Anthea Clarke, Radio Orwell, Ipswich; Mr Peter Claydon, Felixstowe; Mr R. W. Coe, Hadleigh; Mr. R. J. Collis, Lowestoft; Mr Richard Crier, Woodbridge; Mr D. Deas, Bawdsey; Mr John Deller, North Hykeham; Mr Jack Dodman, Ipswich; Mr Terry Dodman, Ipswich; Mr Colin Durrant, Ipswich; *East Anglian Daily Times* and their associated newspapers; Mr C. H. Elliott, Wimbledon; Mr Jim Empson, Anglia Cameras, Ipswich; Mr Stewart Evans, Bury St Edmunds; Mrs Sylvia Evans, London; Mr H. Fairhead, Langley; The Foreign and Commonwealth Office, Hanslope; Mr Roger Freeman, Dedham; Squadron Leader A. German, Bawdsey; Wing Commander and Mrs A. R. Gilding, Keighley; Mr B. G. Goldsmith, B.E.M., Kesgrave; Master Sergeant Vickie Grahame, U.S.A.F.; Mr J. D. Greenwood, Nottingham; Mr D. Hall, Barton Leonard; Mr L. Hanley, Stoke-by-Nayland; Dr Helena Hamilton, Chesterfield; Squadron Leader F. A. Hodges, Theydon Bois; Ipswich and District Historical Transport Society and its ever-helpful members; Mr and Mrs Jeffrey, Bakewell; Mr L. C. Johnson-Jones, Hitchin; Mr G. R. Kiddell, Ipswich; Mrs V. Kilbride, Felixstowe; Mr G. F. Kitchen, Stutton; Mr John Langford, Ipswich; Wing Commander W. G. Lawrence, Hingham; Mr and Mrs Ken Leighton, Ipswich; Mr S. Leslie, Scarborough; Mr E. G. Lipscombe, Gravesend; Mr Robert Malster, Ipswich; Mr L. Martin, Wolverhampton; Mr Roger Maynard, B.B.C. Norwich; Captain Kathleen T.

McCollom, U.S.A.F.; Ministry of Defence (Air); Mr J. H. Morley, O.B.E., Holton; Wing Commander K. A. Mummery, Marlow; Norfolk and Suffolk Aviation Museum, Flixton; Mr and Mrs Reg O'Neil, Walton-on-the-Naze; Mr L. E. Opdycke, Poughkeepsie, U.S.A.; Mr R. V. Perkins, Malvern; Mrs E. Pettitt, Beccles; Mrs D. Phillips, Felixstowe; Miss M. Puttergill, Orford; Lady Margery Quilter, Methersgate; Mrs Gwen Reading, Chandlers Ford; Rolls-Royce (1971) Limited, Derby; Flight Lieutenant P. J. Rowland, West Wickham; The Royal Air Force Association; Flight Lieutenant S. Salmond, Bawdsey; Wing Commander H. J. Sanders, Watford; Miss Margaret Stacey, Redhill; Mr M. Stagg; Suffolk Coastal District Council; Suffolk County Council; the Reverend C. C. Taylor, Temple Fortune; Mr and Mrs B. Tillyer, Fawley; Mr L. Trolley, Weybridge; Wing Commander J. R. Turnbull, M.B.E., A. E., Eastbourne; Mr W. Twiddy, Ipswich; the United States Air Force, Bentwaters and Woodbridge Bases; Mr John Venmore-Rowland, Lavenham; Mr Peter Whatling, Ipswich; Mrs G. H. White, Felixstowe; Mrs E. Whitehair, Lavenham; Squadron Leader W. Williams, Par; Mr G. G. Youett, Mitcham.

My special thanks to Squadron Leader Arthur Williams, surely Bawdsey's longest-serving officer, for honouring me by contributing the foreword. A pioneer in the true sense, Mr A. F. Wilkins, O.B.E., again contributed in full his vivid recollections of the early days at Bawdsey Manor, and these I feel are the true evidence of the development of radar. Mr A. J. R Frost, A.I.I.O., A.R.P.S., M.I.R.T., again gave advice on the photographic material, while Mr C. E. "Holly" Hall produced another of his colourful, attractive jackets for this book.

For her unstinting patience in assisting with the prolonged research required for this book, and checking and cross-checking manuscripts, my deepest gratitude and heartfelt thanks to my wife, Margaret. Her counsel and advice in so many aspects is without measure. Many thanks also to my publishers and their very able staff for their full co-operation, quiet guidance and excellent workmanship.

Gordon Kinsey,
Roundwood Road,
Ipswich,
Suffolk, 1983.

Foreword

by
SQUADRON LEADER ARTHUR WILLIAMS

I RECALL over forty years ago approaching Felixstowe Ferry to cross the River Deben to Royal Air Force Station, Bawdsey for the first time. There was no jetty, no landing stage, so the twenty-stone ferryman, "Tubby" Marjoram, gave me a pick-a-back to save me wet feet.

Little did I know then that I was to remain at Bawdsey until the mid-fifties and to be responsible for the training of many of the men and women who operated the new generations of radar equipment installed both at Bawdsey and at other stations throughout the world.

Walking through the Station today, one's memories flow back to Hut 64, the original Chain Home Operational Hut, no longer there, and to the hours waiting and watching in company with "Tiny" Sewart, Frank Hilditch and John Crellin, to name but three.

Looking towards the sea, one recalls walks through the beautiful Italian Garden, also, alas, no longer to be seen. A little further along one comes on the last remains of the original Chain Home Low aerial bases, now covered with many years' growth of cliff-top bushes. And then one is reminded of how the walled garden provided fresh vegetables and fruit, including grapes, nectarines and peaches grown under glass, for those who wished to purchase them, some of the income helping to maintain a thriving pig farm looked after by "Jockey" Hunt, that well-known local character.

One recalls, too, the happy times spent in the Manor, the dances, the concerts and the children's parties at Christmas; and looking down on the lawn in front of the Manor one also remembers it strewn with telegraph poles and cut by ditches to prevent any possible landing by the enemy.

Later on Nature provided what would have been a natural deterrent to such landings when the area was submerged by the East Coast floods of 1953. The Station then played a big part in organising the efforts of hundreds of airmen who worked to stem the onrush of water, and in the aftermath of the floods we were visited by Prince Philip; and the Commanding Officer, Squadron Leader Theophilus, was awarded the O.B.E.

And so, after serving under thirteen Commanding Officers, the time came for me to bid farewell to this most famous Radar Station. Few of us can have spent so many years on one Station. They were happy years, and now I live with the many happy memories of my sojourn in Suffolk.

Arthur Williams,
Goring-by-Sea.

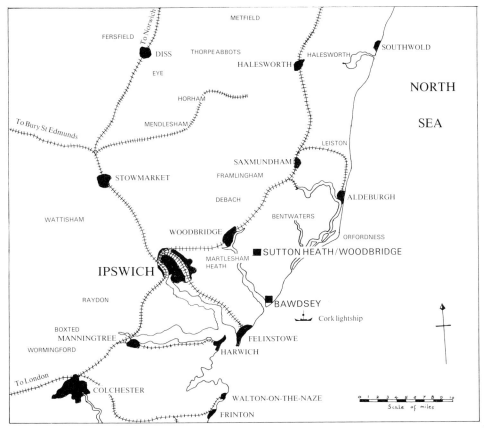

The location of the R.A.F. stations at Bawdsey and Sutton Heath in relation to other Second World War airfields.

The Setting

SUFFOLK'S Heritage Coast is indeed something to be treasured, even if it does lack majestic cliffs and great rock formations jutting into the sea in a frothy confusion of white foam. Here no gently sloping sandy beaches shrink and grow with each successive tide; no coast road skirts the shore. Instead marsh and heath run down to the sea, maintaining an almost sea-level flatness for some distance inland, and the sparse population huddles in villages set almost out of earshot of the breaking seas which roar and crash on the shingle.

This is strange terrain, with sea and river running cheek-by-jowl, sometimes only yards apart; a desolate area of shingle and sand, set with wild spiky sea grasses and cut by twisting creeks of oozing mud. Only the dismal cries of innumerable seabirds break the silence.

Here the smuggler's art was developed. Many a cargo was run on this bleak, windswept coast which has its southern extremity at the mouth of the River Deben. In the eighteen or so miles from Aldeburgh to Bawdsey there is only the village of Orford sprawling along the river behind Orfordness and the lonely hamlet of Shingle Street, making this a lonely and secluded area.

Right at the southern end of this stretch of coast stands Bawdsey Manor, topping the 70-foot promontory which rises like a mountain above the flatness all around. Started during 1890 and completed in 1904, it was the home of the Quilter family, who lived there until it was sold to the Air Ministry in 1936, the Manor, 168 acres of land, outbuildings and estate cottages becoming Air Ministry property for a mere £24,000.

It was here that development work on radio location, later known as radar, was carried out, ideas were translated into workable devices and a band of scientists and technicians fused into one of the finest teams in history. Here new sciences were created and new techniques taught.

This was not the first time that the Manor had provided military accommodation, for during the First World War the grounds and stables had been requisitioned by the Devonshire Regiment.

Bawdsey Manor is of architectural interest because it is a concoction of varying styles employed by the assortment of architects involved in its design. These styles range from early Dutch to the more modern additions which comprise a pseudo Elizabethan Red Tower and an Oriental White

With Bawdsey Manor in the background, air-women march past the reviewing officer, the Earl of Bandon, in 1951. *Mrs M. Beck*

1

Tower, connected by a Gothic front. It is used as station headquarters, airwomen's barracks, and Officers' Mess.

One of the five operational stations guarding the air approaches to London, it carried out to the full its wartime duties. As new types of radar were developed most stations specialized in one type of equipment, but Bawdsey Manor possessed them all and was by far the most important British radar station during the war. Several times it served as the site of the prototype for new systems which were successfully brought to operational status, and although it was the oldest radar station in the world, it was also always the most up-to-date.

Just a few miles up the road, set deep amid the dense dark conifers of Forestry Commission plantations and rolling heathland, R.A.F. Woodbridge, the 1939-1945 wartime Sutton Heath, known by one name or the other to the majority of R.A.F. and U.S.A.A.F. aircrews, still goes about its business. It is the home of aircraft which if the necessity ever arose could be used for the combined N.A.T.O. defence of this realm, while giant transports and helicopters stand ever ready at a moment's notice to wing their way on errands of mercy.

Over four decades on from the opening events of this history, the scene remains much as it did at the beginning, and the same air of secrecy still prevails, giving the first-time visitor a feeling that something different happened here and indeed could still be happening. Protected areas prevent exploration of these historic sites, a necessary restriction as both Bawdsey and Sutton Heath are still in military occupation, but on the infrequent occasions of "open days" the public are able to see some of the environments described in the following pages.

Bawdsey Manor simmers in the sun. In this view from the top of one of the radar towers the Manor can be clearly identified in the centre. *Mrs Gwen Reading*

CHAPTER ONE

Early Warnings

AIR RAIDS on the British Isles were something new when on 31st May, 1915, the German Zeppelin L.35 under the command of Hauptmann Linnarz ventured as far as the East End of London, dropped 3,000 lb. of high explosive, killed seven people, injured thirty more and caused considerable damage to property. Its passage was not greatly hampered by the defences, as it is reported that at this time London's anti-aircraft defences amounted to twelve guns.

Up to that time no successes had been scored against raiders and only one had been reported damaged. During 1916, however, a belt of seachlights stretching from the South Coast to Northumberland had been sited approximately 25 miles inland. Intercepting aircraft patrolled the inner side of this light belt, hoping to spot any intruder as it passed through the illuminated area.

Observer posts connected by telephone to a central reporting centre attempted to give some advance warning, and a crude form of sound detector was also employed. This was only partially effective, as its use was limited to periods when the raider's engines were running, and the Zeppelin being a lighter-than-air machine was able to throttle back or switch off its motive power and drift silently along.

A new threat to the cities and towns of Southern and Eastern England appeared during December, 1917, when the Germans used the long-winged Straken Giant bomber on raids against this country. Powered by four 260 h.p. Maybach motors and with an endurance of seven hours and a top speed of 78 m.p.h., this aircraft carried a bomb load almost three times that of the previous aircraft raiders, the twin-engined Gotha. The Giant also carried new equipment such as multi-machine-gun positions and wireless.

The majority of the raids were made on moonlit nights, for better recognition of the targets, but on the few occasions when the raiders ventured forth on dark nights they were identified quite effectively by R.F.C. and R.N.A.S. patrolling aircraft whose crews located them by their engine noise and exhaust flares. Defences to cope with these new raiders came into operation during the middle of 1918, far too late as the last raid on London had taken place on the night of 19th May. Out of thirty-three aircraft which set forth that night to create terror and destruction in the London area, only thirteen reached the capital; six were shot down, three of them by fighters and the others by anti-aircraft fire.

The 103 raids made on the United Kingdom during the First World War resulted in the deaths of 1,413 people, another 3,407 being injured. In the Greater London area casualty figures were 670 killed and 1,970 injured. These operations cost the Germans ten airships and twenty-two aeroplanes.

No advance warning system had been devised to give the defences adequate notice of the approach of raiders, and this situation remained for some time. Eventually radio communication from the defending fighters to their bases enabled information to be passed on to Anti-Aircraft Command headquarters. It is interesting to note that at this time the responsibility for air raid warning was spread between Anti-Aircraft Command, the Royal Defence Corps and the Metropolitan Observation Service under Lieutenant-Commander H. Paget, O.B.E., R.N.V.R. The R.D.C. had its Anti-Aircraft Section under an Army officer, Major General Ashmore, with Brigadier-General Huggins as the Royal Air Force Commander.

During 1922 the defensive system was split up when the War Office relinquished overall responsibility and passed it on to the Air Ministry, although the former still provided the necessary guns and searchlights. Various successive Air Force Schemes provided for specific numbers of fighter squadrons, but due to a continuing need for economies they always fell short of requirements. Nevertheless, a great deal of emphasis was placed on fighter aircraft, a large proportion of which were to be designed as day and night fighters.

In East Anglia the need for detection of aircraft for defence purposes brought about the formation during June, 1922, of the Observer Corps from the Defence Corps. No. 18 Group was formed after a meeting in the General Post Office Exchange at Colchester, Essex.

Captain Walden Hammond and ladies of a yachting party picnic on Bawdsey Beach in 1919. The Ferry Cottages can be seen in the background.   *Mrs M. Martin*

During 1925, a defence system known as the Air Defence of Great Britain was set up under the command of Air Marshal Sir John Salmond. Fighter squadrons for interception duties were stationed at only one airfield in East Anglia, Duxford in Cambridgeshire, where there were No. 19 Squadron equipped with the Gloster Grebe, No. 29 Squadron with the same type of aircraft and No. 41 Squadron which flew the Armstrong-Whitworth Siskin. Both these aircraft were single-seat fighters with air-cooled radial engines, equipped with wireless and night flying aids, the Siskin being the faster with a top speed of 156 m.p.h. Armament was the usual twin Vickers 0.303-inch machine-guns mounted in the front fuselage and firing through the airscrew arc.

In order to back up the members of the Observer Corps, members of H.M. Coastguard were also trained in air observation duties with the posts at Orfordness, Suffolk, and Walton-on-the-Naze, Essex, covering the approaches to East Anglia.

The Army through its Army Acoustic Section endeavoured during the mid-1920s to bring into action more advanced sound detection devices. These ranged from mechanical "ears" through crude electrical gadgets to a system which to many appeared at the time "out of this world". It consisted of large, curved concrete walls to act as sound mirrors ranging in size from fifteen-foot diameter structures to a massive sloping wall 200 feet long and 26 feet high. When tested these "mirrors" reflected the sound of an approaching aircraft approximately three times louder, but gave no indication whatever of its height or direction. Another disadvantage was that they were not able to be sound selective and they also amplified any local noises which occurred at the time of the aircraft's approach, and therefore their use was extremely hazardous. As a memorial to these experiments, a 200-foot wall and two 25-foot diameter "mirrors" still stand on Romney Marsh in Kent. A little further along the coast between Lympne and Hythe, on a hillside at Dolmarsh, stand two more large "mirrors".

Parallel with the foregoing experiments was an Army sponsored experiment known as the "Fixed Azimuth System". Operated in conjunction with Observer Corps posts, it was a telephone-orientated system utilising a base line between two posts from which coded calls were received and plotted on a grid-screen which recorded the height and position of the aircraft under observation. This information was then fed into an early form of computer which rejoiced in the nickname of the "Fruit Machine". With the parallel development of radio location further growth of the "Fixed Azimuth System" was halted.

The day of the electric sound detector was not wholly past in 1936, however, for in that year the Army supplied the Observer Corps posts at Walton-on-the-Naze, Thorpe-le-Soken, and West Mersea, all in Essex, with a

Off-duty personnel from Martlesham Heath swimming in the River Deben at high tide.

Mrs M. Martin

device known as the Amplifier Sound Detector Unit. This was a more sophisticated form of detection equipment comprising double and treble resonated microphones used in conjunction with a low frequency amplifier and loudspeaker system. One advantage of this unit was that it was substantially constructed to enable it to be employed on field duties and it could be operated by personnel with little or no knowledge of wireless. Again the equipment was not really sound selective and local sound sources were amplified along with the target sound, thus making the device only partially efficient, and the project was dropped during the autumn of 1936.

Visual sighting by the Observer Corps and its predecessor the Royal Defence Corps was the sole source of aircraft movement observation in the 1920s and 1930s, and although the R.A.F. considered the work of the Corps to be excellent, that was not the view widely held in other high places. This was borne out during 1930 when the Chief Constable of Colchester stated that he doubted the usefulness of the Observer Corps and thought that its future was limited.

Air exercises in successive years showed up the deficiencies in aircraft detection. In the mid-thirties Orfordness was deemed to be the northerly limit of threat should an enemy approach from the Low Countries or France, but during 1938 as it became clear that the threat was coming from Germany herself the limit was moved up to the Humber and Air Exercises for that year covered Lincolnshire as well as the south and east.

In the meantime work had been going on apace at Orfordness with the development of radio location, a story told in *Orfordness — Secret Site*,* of which this publication is in part a continuation. Radio location, or radar as it was later called, worked on the principal of reflection of radiated radio waves from objects towards which they had been directed. In the main it was

Orfordness — Secret Site by Gordon Kinsey, published by Terence Dalton Limited, 1981.

6

operated in much the same way as a searchlight, picking up an object in the dark, revealing things which would not normally be seen in non-visible conditions. One can liken it to the phenomena of sound, in that on a dark night in the vicinity of tall cliffs the sound of clapped hands will be returned to the sender, thus indicating the position of the cliffs. As the speed of sound is known, if the interval between clap and echo were timed the distance to the objective could be calculated. Likewise radio location could be used for calculating distance since like the speed of sound the speed of radio signals is also known.

An Army sound detector at work.

Experimentation had started in Great Britain during 1920 with the formation by the Department of Scientific and Industrial Research of a Radio Research Board under the leadership of Admiral Sir Henry Jackson. Early work involved assisting Professor Edward Appleton*, the British physicist, with his research into the ionosphere. Appleton gave his name to the layer of ionized gases more than 100 miles above the earth's surface.

The ionosphere is divided into three layers, the first or D layer 30-56 miles above the surface; the E or Heaviside layer, named after another British physicist, Oliver Heaviside, 56-100 miles above the surface; and the F or Appleton layer, above 100 miles. These layers are useful in reflecting back radio waves of differing frequencies, the Heaviside layer in the main reflecting the medium wavelength signals while the Appleton layer reflects long wave transmissions. Without these layers long-distance transmissions of waves beamed in a straight line would be impossible as the waves would disappear into space.

All this formed a basis for the work done at Orfordness and to be brought to a successful conclusion at Bawdsey Manor.

*Sir Edward Victor Appleton, K.C.B., F.R.S. (1892-1965), who gained the Nobel Prize for Physics in 1947.

CHAPTER TWO

Chain Home

THESE next two chapters are told by Mr A. F. Wilkins, O.B.E., a pioneer from the very first days and colleague of Robert Watson Watt. The author is greatly honoured that Mr Wilkins has recalled those days of trial and error, success and disappointment for us all to share.

During August or September, 1935, it became apparent that the accommodation at Orfordness would soon become inadequate and that extra space would have to be found. One afternoon in that period Watson Watt, E. G. Bowen and I set off in Watson Watt's car to look over the Martello Tower at the Aldeburgh end of the Orfordness peninsula as it was thought that this might provide the room we required.

The tower was very soon rejected, and as we walked away Watson Watt asked if we had any other proposals. It so happened that at the end of our first week at Orfordness, Airey and I had gone off to explore the country around and by chance found ourselves at Bawdsey Ferry. On that beautiful spring afternoon with the sun shining out of a clear blue sky and the River Deben lying placid at low water, we both fell in love with the place and especially with the Manor standing close to the river mouth. This seemed to me an ideal spot for a research station if ever we should have to leave Orfordness. Unfortunately, however, the house was occupied, and so were several other houses on the large estate. Before leaving Bawdsey we ascertained that the house belonged to Sir Cuthbert Quilter, who also owned other large houses in the district.

It was this visit that I remembered as we drove away from Aldeburgh. I told Watson Watt that I could show him the ideal place but that it might not be for sale. He decided nevertheless to see it and we set off immediately. I remember that journey well because we were riding in a 15 h.p. Daimler car which Watson Watt had recently bought. As we drove along I said to him "I see that these cars have a fluid flywheel which permits one to go into reverse at 60 m.p.h. and all that happens is that the car rapidly decelerates and then moves off backwards." "That's interesting," said Watson Watt, "shall we try it?" And he did there and then, and it behaved just as I had said!

The Chain Home transmitter aerial towers seen from the top of a receiver tower. The Chain Home Low aerial can be seen on the lower platform of the nearest tower. *Mrs Sylvia Evans*

When we arrived at Bawdsey Ferry Watson Watt was so charmed with the Manor, as Airey and I had been, that he requested the Air Ministry to find out whether the owner would be willing to sell it. To our delight Sir Cuthbert seemed quite ready to do this and move into one of his smaller houses. The Air Ministry bought the whole estate for £24,000.

The single 250-foot lattice receiving mast at Bawdsey was begun as soon as the sale of the estate to the Air Ministry had been completed and it was finished in early March, 1936. It had a cross of 4 inch by 4 inch timbers on top intended to take the two dipoles for the Direction Finder. The foreman of Messrs. Harland and Wolff, the contractors, declared the mast complete one Saturday morning while Watson Watt, C. M. Minnis, A. J. Muir and myself were present in the hut at its base. So anxious were we to discover by how much the performance of the system had been improved with the aerial at 250 feet that I volunteered to make the first ascent of the mast to install the aerials, seated in the bosun's chair made by the Air Ministry Works Directorate.

The chair had been designed to last a lifetime; the frame was made of one-inch diameter steel rod which held a thick oak seat and a heavy steel circular band, presumably to prevent one from falling off and through which one had to climb before sitting down. The dimensions of the whole contraption had been arranged so that it would go through the top section of the mast, the cross-sectional area of which was smaller than that of the other two sections. Unfortunately no account had been made of the passenger's knees and I soon found out on that first ascent that one had to be something of a contortionist to negotiate the top section while remaining in the chair. It was, furthermore, quite impossible to work on the aerial when the chair was at its highest point and I had to squeeze out of the chair and stand on the face of the mast while installing the aerials and connecting them to the open wire lines which I had taken up with me.

On completing the work I was not sorry to give the signal to Watson Watt and his assistants to wind me down to contemplate the mess into which my beautiful new grey flannel trousers had got through contact with the wet creosote of the mast. Later ascents were made with a home-made and simpler bosun's chair, the top section being climbed without it.

In March, 1936, at the time we began to install the receiver by this mast, Watson Watt told me that the Air Ministry were considering whether to spend more money, I think he mentioned £100,000, on further concrete sound locators, of the type which had been built experimentally on Romney Marsh and which had proved completely inadequate. He thought that if we could show the Royal Air Force that Radio Direction Finding (R.D.F.) could track an aircraft to a range of 100 km, no further concrete mirrors would be built. There was then a rush to see whether the Orfordness transmitter and Bawdsey receiver combination could give this performance.

A view along Felixstowe golf links towards Bawdsey showing the first two aerial towers at
Bawdsey Research Station, as the establishment was then known. *Mr E. Nevill*

During the summer of 1935, L. H. Bainbridge-Bell had returned to the
Radio Research Establishment to develop a Cathode Ray Direction Finding
(C.R.D.F.) receiver for ultimate use on R.D.F. By March, 1936, he had
reached a position of having two similar receivers which he was just starting to
test. Unfortunately he was still very pessimistic about the final outcome, as he
considered stability of performance of receivers at 20-30 Mhz* to be unlikely.
It may have been this pessimism which caused him to hand one over to us
without a fight when he was approached by Watson Watt for a receiver to be
used in the experiment at Bawdsey.

This test was conducted during March, 1936, after Bainbridge-Bell's
receiver had been set up. A single Hawker Hart biplane flew as usual at 15,000
feet from Orfordness to Bircham Newton in North Norfolk, a distance of
108 km, but this time we asked the pilot to continue across the Wash to
Skegness and then to return on the same path. Minnis and I observed at
Bawdsey and were able to attain a range of 130 km with position finding the
whole way.

I reported this satisfactory result to Watson Watt. It is possible that it
resulted in the scrapping of the project to construct more concrete mirror
locators, and it may be that the existing mirrors on the Kent coast were also
then discarded.

The 250-foot high aerials used at this time were designed for use on
13 Mhz. It had been found that signal interference and atmospherics on the
original frequency of 6 Mhz were at times very heavy and a change to 13 Mhz

*Mhz — Megahertz.

11

was made during the autumn of 1935. Conditions on the new frequency were better, but signal interference was troublesome at times.

Decisions as to the working frequency were made quite arbitrarily; I know of no request for allocations being made to the Post Office then or later, and we never heard of any complaints of our interfering with commercial services.

Development on 13 Mhz proceeded until October, 1936, when a change to 22 Mhz took place. This evolved in the following circumstances. In September, 1935, we were joined by H. Dewhurst, a Scientific Officer from the Royal Aircraft Establishment, so he was asked to begin the development of a transportable R.D.F. installation for use at mobile bases (M.B.). As the height of his aerials would be limited by portability requirements to somewhere between 70 and 100 feet, he decided, with the object of keeping the main lobe of the aerial radiation pattern low, to use a frequency of 22 Mhz. This was, of course, sensible from the signal interference point of view as there was relatively little commercial traffic round that frequency at the time. Dewhurst's subsequent experiments showed that 22 Mhz was very suitable in that aircraft echo strengths did not appear to be significantly reduced. After the near failure of the main (13 Mhz) R.D.F. station during the September, 1936, Air Exercises it was decided to make considerable modifications in the equipment; one of these was a change to Dewhurst's original frequency of 22 Mhz, he having in the meantime selected an even higher frequency.

While tests were being conducted using the 250-foot array at Orfordness, certain shortcomings of the transmitter began to manifest themselves. During flights it was noticed that the echo strength suddenly dropped due to a change

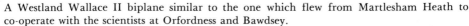

A Westland Wallace II biplane similar to the one which flew from Martlesham Heath to co-operate with the scientists at Orfordness and Bawdsey.

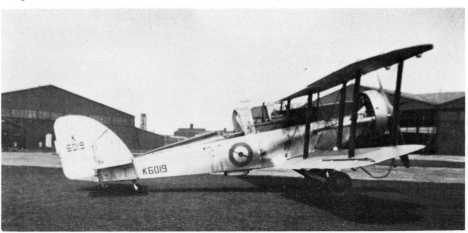

of frequency. On one such occasion a visit from the Tizard Committee was in progress and I was demonstrating an echo from the test aircraft to Professor Blackett and was feeling very pleased with the quite high signal-to-noise ratio seen. Suddenly there was a big drop in strength which I could not recover by re-tuning. Blackett knew the transmitter was in the early days of development and no harm was done by this unfortunate incident.

Bowen blamed "my lines" and aerials for the trouble and even went so far as to claim large losses in the lines, which were open 200 lb copper wire supported by standard Post Office insulators designed for similar lines. No change was made until Bowen's transfer to full-time work on airborne R.D.F. (RDF 2) in the spring of 1936, when J. H. Mitchell was given the transmitter work. Unfortunately he had no previous experience and his oscillator and amplifier set was not a practical proposition. On his transfer to other work the transmitter problem was given to H. Larnder, whose efforts soon produced a set, the output of which he gave as 25 Kw peak pulse power.

A good deal of argument occurred about how to measure output power. Bowen used a resistance potential divider across the output terminals of the set and with a cathode ray tube measured the voltage set up across part of the resistance. He claimed powers of up to 100 Kw. Larnder tried several methods but finally settled for the well-known one in which the transmitter power is applied to a strip lamp placed alongside a similar lamp supplied from the mains. The power necessary to heat the filament of the mains lamp to the same brilliance as the other lamp enables the r.f. power to be obtained. From the results gathered on aircraft echoes we concluded that "100 Bowen kilowatts equalled 25 Larnder kilowatts".

Larnder was later joined by Whelpton, and between them they developed a transmitter which was subsequently used by Metropolitan Vickers at the early Chain Home stations. Whelpton had several of his sets made up in the Bawdsey workshops and they were used at the first five (Thames Estuary) Chain Home Stations.

By December, 1935, after seven months' work we had developed a transmitter of 100 Kw (nominal) peak pulse power which worked with a pulse width of about 15 microseconds. The receiver was adequate in gain and bandwidth. Performance on aircraft range finding with this equipment was such that, on a single aircraft flying at 7,000 feet, detection could be achieved at 70 km to an accuracy of half a kilometre; the corresponding range at 15,000 feet flying height was 85 kilometres. Ranges to which aircraft could be followed were somewhat greater and these results were obtained with 70-foot masts.

A crude direction-finding system had been tried and there seemed to be no reason why a properly engineered system should not perform well. In addition to measuring range and bearing, height had also been measured by a system which required considerable development. Such was the situation when on 19th December, 1935, we were told that the Treasury had sanctioned a chain of five R.D.F. stations for use in the defence of London.

A recommendation had been made previously (September, 1935) by the Air Defence Sub-Committee of the Committee of Imperial Defence that, as progress in the development of R.D.F. had proceeded much faster than expected, a chain of stations could be built to cover the coast from the Tyne to Southampton and it was presumably this recommendation, modified as regards the cover to be provided, which now received Treasury approval. In retrospect this is amazing since no prototype R.D.F. station existed to convince the Treasury that the proposed chain of stations would give value for their quite considerable cost. That the money was forthcoming at such a comparatively early stage in the technical development was clearly indicative of the urgency with which R.D.F. was required and also showed that the Air Council had accepted the advice of the Tizard Committee that there was no practical reason why R.D.F. should not perform successfully as set down in the Watson Watt Memoranda.

It was particularly remarkable in the case of the recommendations by the Air Defence Sub-Committee as the apparatus was then in the earliest stages of development and in particular, no means had yet been prepared for direction finding, without which it was thought that position fixing would have to be performed by range cutting using adjacent stations.

Initially the crossed dipole method of direction finding had been proposed, but by the time the design of the Estuary Chain began it seems that little reliance was placed on its accuracy. This was not surprising, as what little experience had been obtained was confined to the crude array at Orfordness and later at Bawdsey. It was now decided to use both D.F. and range cutting for the new chain, while for height measurement the aerial layout permitted the use of horizontally-opposed aerials for elevation finding.

The technical requirements for the stations were that they be placed as high as possible above sea level, but that there should be a reasonable flat landscape on the seaward side, a requirement of the elevation finding method. Spacing of about 25 miles was envisaged to give a reasonable operational overlap.

Early in 1936 Watson Watt requested me to consider the siting of the stations bearing these requirements in mind. Bawdsey was to be the most northerly; it would be provided with one 247-foot wooden transmitting tower and two similar receiving towers and would perform range, direction and elevation measurement. Southwards, the next station would have a transmitter tower only and would be used for range cutting with Bawdsey, or its next southerly neighbour. Third and fifth stations would be similar to Bawdsey, while the fourth would transmit only. The second and fourth sites did not have to be situated on flat land.

Two of the four Chain Home aerial towers at Great Bromley seen after the war, when the nearer one was being demolished. *East Anglian Daily Times*

I made site proposals for the four new stations to Watson Watt after a map search with Minnis, and Watson Watt gave his approval. My next move was to the Air Ministry Works Directorate, who gave their approval, and the sites were readily acquired except for the one next to Bawdsey which was a golf course. However an excellent alternative was quickly found at Great Bromley, Essex. The initial five stations of the chain were (1) Bawdsey, Suffolk, (2) Great Bromley, Essex, (3) Canewdon, Essex, (4) Dunkirk, Kent, and (5) Dover, also in Kent.

Range-cutting died a slow death partly due, I think, to the invention by a Corporal Chapman, one of the early R.A.F. trainees for R.D.F. duties, of a procedure subsequently referred to as "The Chapman Scheme". This was towards the end of 1936. The scheme involved the provision at direction-finder-equipped stations such as Bawdsey, Canewdon and Dover of two cathode ray tubes for the operator to observe. One would display echoes from his own transmitter and the other echoes from the adjacent transmitter-only station. The operator had to turn his goniometer and note the two echoes, one on each tube, which attained minima at the same goniometer setting. It was hoped thus to resolve ambiguity. The position of the aircraft giving rise to the two echoes would thus be found in terms of the ranges read on the tubes and the distance between the two stations. As the direction finder was not required to give bearings its accuracy was of little importance.

The Chapman Scheme was quite attractive in the situation then existing and it would doubtless have been used in the chain had it not been found that direction finder and ranges gave adequate plan position information. I do not recall any test of the scheme or, indeed, of plain range-cutting.

When the Great Bromley transmitter was put into operation after several long delays when building the aerial tower, we often received the direct pulse at Bawdsey and noted that it was subject to small but irritating jitter as observed on the cathode ray tube. The Chapman Scheme was still envisaged at this time and R. J. Dippy made up his "Spongy Lock", an electronic flywheel which he installed in the time-phase circuit of the cathode ray tube displaying the Great Bromley signal. By this time we were so rushed preparing equipment for the 1936 Air Exercises to be held in September that we did not have time to test the Chapman Scheme.

Watson Watt had decided now that self-supporting wooden towers would be used for the transmitting and receiving aerials and that these would be 247 feet high. The designer of these towers is not certain but was probably Mr Garnish, of the Air Ministry Works Branch, who was responsible for liaison with the contractors, and Mr Lutkin of the Radio Research School was also involved. The contractors for the tower masts at all the Chain Stations were Messrs C. F. Elwell, who had great experience in constructional wooden structures. When erection began it became apparent that the foreman at each site would be responsible for working out his own methods as no standard procedures existed and each site had its own difficulties. This contributed partly to the slow progress of the work.

Bawdsey, Canewdon and Dover were to be ready for the Air Exercises of September, 1936, and this created problems in that the apparatus had to be built at Bawdsey, or in the case of the receivers, at the R.R.S. In normal circumstances one would have anticipated a reasonable period for trials before taking part in anything as serious as the Air Exercises, when all the "top eyes" of the Royal Air Force would be on the new equipment and a failure might have jeopardised the whole future of R.D.F. These, however, were not normal times, and I think it true to say that no part of the equipment with which the Estuary Chain and the later Intermediate Chain were equipped had been subjected to any of the pre-installation tests normally required for military equipment.

The start of the 1936 Exercises marked as far as I was concerned the beginning of the period when installation and putting into service of Chain Stations had to take precedence over research and the development of aerials. The result of this was that the aerials, especially those for receiving, on which the D.F. and elevation accuracy depended, were indeed "third best". According to Watson Watt's dictum, we had "to give them something to be going on with".

The systems proposed for these Exercises were to work on about 13 Mhz. Three receivers were built at R.R.S. and five transmitters at Bawdsey. No aerial installations could be started until the towers were well advanced, and in the event progress on these was so slow that it was decided to operate only the Bawdsey station during the Exercises. A six-element aerial array was eventually installed on the transmitter tower and a three-element crossed-aerial array for the receiver. No elevation equipment was operational as the second tower was nowhere near completion.

In the receiving room, which was part of the Manor stables, we installed three receivers in parallel as a standby, "belt and braces" step. This enabled several observers to be used simultaneously and these were so used on the first day of the Exercises. The first observers that day were Watson Watt, Dewhurst, Hanbury Brown and myself, and I recall that silence reigned throughout except for occasional range observations by Watson Watt which recalled to me his single observation at Orfordness during the first Tizard Committee visit.*

The complete absence of echoes was certainly odd and a full inspection of the apparatus failed to reveal the cause. After the first afternoon's watch I chanced to look out of the receiver room window and was amazed to see several workmen sitting on the aerials. Although the workmen were removed from the transmitter tower and its thousands of volts, their presence did not explain the lack of initial success. Later observations during the exercises were made with the same receiving gear but we reverted to the Orfordness transmitter and the 250-foot aerial array, and reasonable results were obtained.

The Exercises thus proved very discouraging, especially after all the preparations and hard work, but in retrospect R.D.F. should never have been used at this time—we were nowhere near ready. It was fortunate that the part played by the older equipment in the latter stages of the Exercises was enough to convince the Air Council of R.D.F.'s value. I think that Tizard was somewhat shaken by the happenings. I saw him and Watson Watt leaving the

*See *Orfordness—Secret Site*, page 145.

Manor immediately after the Exercises and overheard Tizard say "and remember, Watson Watt, much depends on you".

We were informed that the Chain was to take part in the next Exercises scheduled for the following April (1937), and this time we were determined to put up a good showing. Technical lessons had been learnt, we had introduced updated equipment and a change in frequency from 13 Mhz to 22 Mhz was deemed necessary in view of the heavy interference on the lower frequency. A serious trouble was transmitter instability and so Larnder and Whelpton, who

Vickers Valentia K.3603 of the A.&A.E.E. at Martlesham Heath carried out a great number of "request flights" for the Bawdsey scientists.   *Vickers Limited*

had taken over transmitter development from Bowen, were duly instructed to have suitable amplifier-oscillator transmitters ready in good time.

On the receiver side, directional ambiguity was a source of criticism from the Royal Air Force and needed attention. As only one tower was available during the 1936 trials no height information had been available and this had to be remedied for April, 1937. I had been using open-wire 600 ohm transmission lines for both transmitter and receiver and suggested to Watson Watt that it was time that we changed to co-axial cable, but unfortunately neither of us knew where suitable cable was to be obtained.

My responsibilities still included all aerials and the provision of D.F. and elevation measurement and installation at the five stations, so it can be seen that we had an extremely heavy programme over the next six months. At this time I decided that the new 22 Mhz receiving aerials would use both 240-foot towers. The D.F. aerials would be on one tower and the height system on the other, and both sets of aerials would be connected to the receiver in the old stables by co-axial cable. A problem was that this type of cable was non-existent. The London-Birmingham co-axial telephone cable was four high-grade co-axial cores made by The Standard Telephone and Cable

Company Limited, and I visited this company to inquire whether they would be able to supply the cores separately with suitable lead outer, and was very pleased to hear that they could do so. From the data supplied, however, it appeared that if the cable was used on the towers its weight would amount to a few tons, and this was out of the question as Watson Watt learned from the Air Ministry Works Directorate that the towers were fully loaded with their own weight. Although we could not use this cable on the towers an order was placed for runs from tower bases to receiver, and excellent cable it proved to be.

On the towers we used a type of co-axial line which the Post Office were using at this time in short lengths; information regarding this came from T. Walmsley who had, I believe, designed it himself. It used quarter-inch diameter copper tube supplied by the Yorkshire Copper Company, through which was pulled a length of 100 lb copper wire to which were fitted cylindrical insulating beads at two-inch intervals. We borrowed a tool for kinking the copper wire and Airey copied it in the Bawdsey workshops. A working party of Minnis, Carter, Muir and myself, with occasional help from Watson Watt, laboured on after working hours to fix the beads to the wire, a big job, but easy compared with the making up of the line itself. When pulling the wire into the tube it was found that the cylindrical beads abraded the soft copper of the tube itself and a good deal of copper dust built up inside the line. Undaunted, the same team completed the required lengths of line and installed them on the towers, but that was by no means the end of our troubles with co-axial lines for these stations. Problems of one kind or another presented themselves and persisted until well into the Second World War and various experts were brought in to try to solve them.

Life was somewhat easier after we changed from quarter-inch to three-eighths-inch diameter tube of a harder copper and used triangular section insulating beads. Compressed air was used to clear the copper dust or dirt, and fewer instances of short circuits were experienced.

Adjustments of all aerials were hindered by lack of test instruments, as no impedance bridges for our frequency existed. Somewhat later we heard that a former E.M.I. engineer, a Mr H. G. Atkins, had developed an impedance bridge for a frequency range which unfortunately finished some way below 15 Mhz. I went to see him in his "works" at the bottom of his garden in Kew and got him to accept an order for an instrument covering a band up to 30 Mhz. After a long time delay the instrument was delivered and found to work up to 20 Mhz only, and Atkins was unable to improve on this. We had perforce to adjust the aerials as best we could without such instruments.

The D.F. aerials were tested well before April, 1937, and very good results were obtained using Larnder's "25 Kw" transmitter which fed the array through a long transmission line which we took great pains to match accurately to the array. The system was calibrated by flying an aircraft in a straight line away from Bawdsey and at a constant height. Range and elevation readings were automatically fed into an ingenious optical convertor invented by Bainbridge-Bell which gave the height directly. The same convertor when fed with range and azimuth gave the aircraft's plan position (map grid reference).

Soon after the elevation system was completed, two incidents occurred by chance which greatly encouraged Minnis and myself. Just before the lunchtime break one morning the transmitter and receiver were still working after a flight trial. We had been communicating with the aircraft and the radio telephony receiver was in the R.D.F. receiver room. While idly turning its knobs I picked up what I thought to be signals from the daily meteorological flight from Mildenhall in the north of the county. The aircraft was giving its height in thousands of feet at regular intervals and I asked Minnis to notice whether the aircraft could be seen on R.D.F.; he picked it up at once at a range of about 45 miles. He then proceeded to measure its height and the heights indicated by his instruments coincided exactly with those announced by the aircraft's pilot.

The second incident occurred on another day when Minnis and I were observing the R.D.F. shortly before closing down at midday. We noticed a long echo at about 15 miles range, and its height was measured at 20,000 feet, greater than anything so far experienced. We continued to observe and saw that the height was slowly decreasing until the echo finally disappeared at approximately the position of Felixstowe. The echo must have been from a flying boat, but the great height seemed against this conclusion. After lunch I telephoned the Marine Aircraft Experimental Establishment at Felixstowe and was told that they had indeed been flying at 20,000 feet with a specially lightened flying boat.

In the Chain Stations we used two arrays at the transmitter at heights of 220 feet and 80 feet and, at the receiver, a main D.F. array at a mean height of about 220 feet and a gap-filling aerial at about 80 feet. Height was measured with these two aerials or with the 80-foot aerial and another at 40 feet. The actual heights of all these aerials was settled having regard to the contours of the sites.

When the first transmitting array on a 360-foot steel tower was completed at Bawdsey it was thought advisable to measure its horizontal radiation pattern in view of the possibility of distortion due to the pressure of the power (the aerial was suspended between the upper and centre cantilevers). The measurements were made by E. B. Ewing in an R.A.F. motor launch on a rather choppy sea. I was therefore very surprised when Ewing delivered what might have been the theoretical diagram for a half wave aerial, with indications that there was little scatter in his readings; this in spite of the rough sea and the fact that this was the first practical work he had done since leaving school. He saw that I was sceptical of the results but he stoutly denied any "editing" when he arrived back on land. No repeat of these measurements was immediately possible and, as flying tests indicated no gross distortion of the pattern, we let the matter rest.

Bawdsey's neighbouring station, Great Bromley, was used for transmission only, while Canewdon was a complete transmitting and receiving R.D.F. station. Both were prepared for the April, 1937, Air Exercises. Transmitters

Brooke High Speed Launch No. 151 roars along the Suffolk coast. Small craft of this type from R.A.F. Felixstowe carried out a number of operations in connection with the Bawdsey Research Station.   *Mrs M. Tillyer*

were built at Bawdsey, receivers at R.R.S. but modified at Bawdsey, whilst the aerials were installed by an R.A.F. party with assistance from Bawdsey. Calibration of aerials was done by members of my group from Bawdsey. Both stations worked satisfactorily during the Exercises, but I did not have much time to observe them in detail as I was fully occupied with operations at Bawdsey.

About this time Minnis and myself went down to Dover to observe an Avro Anson aircraft fly out to the Wandelaar lightvessel and back. At Dover we plotted quite a good track, "saw" the aircraft turn at the Wandelaar and obtained a good return track. The aircraft was also being tracked by D.F. stations, which were under the direction of Squadron Leader C. K. Chandler, and these gave the impression that the aircraft had violated Belgian airspace. This resulted in a drastic overhaul of the D.F. system.

Whilst at Dover we made another noteworthy observation when echoes were plotted from definite areas in Belgium, which we later discovered were military airfields. This phenomenon was of course an everyday occurrence a few years later when Luftwaffe aircraft were daily plotted circling their bases in France before setting out for England.

The results obtained in the Exercises were gratifying in that the systems for direction finding, height finding, semi-delimitation and gap-filling worked well and could be adapted for any further stations which might be required. They were in fact used at all Chain Home stations until their final scrapping a few years after the end of the war.

The main result of the Exercises was that a decision was made to extend the Chain to cover the whole coastline from the Isle of Wight to the Tay. I was again asked to find suitable sites for all the stations required. The spacing of the stations was settled in terms of the known performance of R.D.F. at different flying heights and the Air Ministry requirement for a gapless R.D.F. frontier at thirty miles from the coast for aircraft flying at 5,000 feet.

The Estuary Chain was designed for optimum performance in the direction of Ostend, as it was considered by the authorities that if war with Germany did break out the enemy would never advance further than that town. This is why we arranged our transmitting dipoles at right angles to the great circle from the station to Ostend.

With Minnis' help I settled the approximate locations of the required stations, and after Watson Watt had given his approval I set off to visit all areas and made firm siting proposals. I was accompanied by R. J. Struthers, of the Air Ministry Works Directorate, Engineering Branch, and an officer of the Lands Branch. It had previously been decided, largely by Watson Watt, that a Standard Chain Station should consist of four 240-foot wooden receiver towers at the corners of a rhombus and four 360-foot steel transmitter towers in line on the extension of a line drawn through the centre of the rhombus parallel to two of its sides. Why Watson Watt decided on the rhombus was never clear. I think that he considered that interaction between receiving aerials would be reduced if that layout were used. The 360-foot steel masts were selected because it would be possible to put on them arrays of similar mean height to the highest receiving aerial. The A.M.W.D. had estimated that their cost would be the same as that of the wooden towers already in use, £2,400 each. The four towers were to carry arrays of different frequencies which would be selected at will as one method of countering jamming. This layout was borne in mind when site-hunting, but there was nothing magic about it and it was only possible to adopt it in five out of six cases.

The sites selected for this extension of the Chain were, to the north, High Street, Darsham, Suffolk; Stoke Holy Cross, Norfolk; West Beckham, Norfolk; Stenigot, Lincolnshire; Staxton Wold, Yorkshire; Danby Beacon, Yorkshire; Ottercops, Northumberland; Drove Hill, Berwick; Douglas Wood, Angus;

and to the south, Rye, Sussex; Pevensey and Poling, both in Sussex; and Ventnor, on the Isle of Wight.

Although at first it was intended that Great Bromley would be a transmitting station only, it was later decided that it would become a full station. Further extensions of the Chain were made soon after the major extension when Prawle Point, Devon, and Nether Button, Orkney, were added, both sites being selected by B. G. Ewing.

Allocation of frequencies for all these stations was made by myself with help from E. W. Seward. In these days of strictly controlled frequency allocations it is amazing to look upon the way Seward and I carried out this task. We decided what the frequencies should be in the band upwards from 22.4 Mhz and we gave no heed to foreign users of frequencies in this band who might be interfered with, deciding only to avoid the television and amateur bands at home. We spaced the frequencies round the Chain so as to minimise mutual interference. The frequencies so chosen were passed to E. J. C. Dixon, who was coordinator of all the work required in building the Chain, and the appropriate aerials, etc., were in due course provided.

The final Chain never used four frequencies per station; I think the usual provision was two sets of aerials for one frequency. During the war aerials were installed at two stations, High Street, Darsham, and Rye, for the highest frequencies on the Wilkins-Seward schedule (about 60 Mhz) so that the general performance at these frequencies could be ascertained. In particular we wanted to know whether their ability to measure smaller angles of elevation was of value. Minnis reported that, in each case, performance was excellent and that height finding started at a greater range than at the lower frequency. At the time of the tests there was not enough effort available to build aerials for these frequencies at other stations and consequently no more use was made of them.

When we started work on R.D.F. in 1935, Watson Watt gave us until the summer of 1938 to have operational equipment, as this was when he expected war with Germany to break out. He was not a long way out.

By September, 1938, there were several stations working with "final" equipment, an engineered version of Larnder and Whelpton's Bawdsey transmitter manufactured by Metropolitan-Vickers and receivers made by Cossor. Both firms had been let in on the R.D.F. secret, and throughout the life of the Chain Stations they were responsible for the equipment.

The R.A.F. Installation Unit under Squadron Leader J. W. Rose erected the aerials and height and D.F. calibrations were made by members of the Wilkins Group. This calibration work was a heavy drain on resources and effectively put an end to all development work on the aerials. For example, plans were put forward to make a thorough investigation into Final Chain aerial systems, and after many delays such a system was ready by the time the

Several Avro Type 671 Rota I autogyros were used to calibrate radar stations on the East Coast.
Flight

Munich Crisis broke out. Minnis looked forward to resuming the work after the emergency, but the day after its completion the supporting tower was struck by lightning and the system wrecked. Time did not allow further work on this job.

Station calibration was originally done by flying aircraft on radial courses out from and back to the station. Ideal for height calibration, but for D.F. not so good unless the aircraft's position could be obtained accurately by requesting it to circle a lightship, and this was not always possible.

During a visit to Bawdsey in about 1938, Lord Rutherford suggested that a better method of calibration would be to use the echo from a dipole hung from a balloon flown from a ship at sea. This was used with great success up to the outbreak of hostilities, which then made this method vulnerable to enemy air attack. Calibration throughout the war was carried out with dipole-carrying autogyro aircraft.

CHAPTER THREE

Identification, Friend or Foe

THE ability of friendly aircraft to identify themselves by means of modified R.D.F. echoes was considered right from the early days, as I had suggested it in a conversation with Watson Watt immediately preceding the writing of his memorandum. The "keyed resonant array" mentioned in that memorandum was claimed by Watson Watt as his idea, and I had on at least one occasion argued with him about it. I recall discussing the fact that if an aircraft behaved like the resonant dipole of my calculations, then another keyed dipole, suitably placed, should alter the strength of the receiver echo.

It was not until 1937 that it became possible to put the proposal to the test. The Army Group at Bawdsey under E. T. Paris was experimenting with R.D.F. for gun-laying (G.L.) and was having some difficulty in following the echo of its own test aircraft when others were present. Dewhurst was having similar trouble when testing his Mobile Base apparatus. Both sets of equipment were operating on about 7 metres wavelength.

Both then decided to experiment with the keyed dipole and Dewhurst agreed to fit the aircraft, an Avro Anson, with a suitable dipole, but no response was achieved on either G.L. or M.B. Rowe, who had then become Superintendent at the Manor, then asked me to try, and I started from scratch, not having seen the arrangement used by Dewhurst on the Anson.

As this aircraft was fitted with a wide-track retractable undercarriage which tucked up into nacelles on its wooden mainplanes, I decided to run the dipole between them, and from its centre, split by an insulator into two quarter waves, ran a length of twin cable to a motor-driven make-and-break device. The twin cable was cut to a suitable number of half waves in electrical length so as to present a short circuit at the dipole centre when the switch was closed. In test the system worked well on both equipments and continued to be used by the Army Group. The installation on the Anson was done by R. H. A. Carter, who also made the switch.

With the arrival of new staff it became possible to begin full-time work on Identification Friend or Foe (I.F.F.). The main problem was to obtain identification on the Chain frequencies, which by then had been placed in the 22-30 Mhz and 40-60 Mhz bands. First of all, keyed dipoles were fitted on flying boats and good results obtained at Bawdsey. The dipole was fitted in the bow of the aircraft, but later tests were made with wires hung between main and tail planes. While carrying out one of these tests, a Supermarine Scapa flying boat from Felixstowe crashed, killing all the crew and our assistant, Hunter Gray. At the subsequent inquiry it was found that airframe failure had caused the fatal crash and the aerial lines were not blameworthy. We also fitted a Handley-Page Heyford bomber with a nose dipole and achieved success. Dowding, who later became Commander-in-Chief, Fighter Command, witnessed one such test and we later heard that he was prepared to request the fitting of dipoles to the whole bomber force.

As I had witnessed all these tests and had concluded the "keying" was adequate for a single aircraft, but useless for a formation as the beating of the echoes would almost mask changes in strength produced by "keying", on

A Supermarine Scapa flying boat on the tarmac at the M.A.E.E., Felixstowe.

Mrs M. Tillyer

hearing of Dowding's proposal I went to see Rowe, expressed my fears and suggested that we should start work on powered I.F.F. so as to provide an amplified response. Rowe was certainly convinced and told me to lose no time in starting to develop a suitable apparatus.

Rowe had a habit of naming an investigation as "the most important job on the Station" and paying a daily visit to those working on it to ensure that they were also regarding it in the same light. Thus powered I.F.F. came into this category and must have been considered of such importance by Rowe that, in addition to putting my group on the job, he also instructed Preist and Taylor to work on it at the same time. Watson Watt had previously taken out a patent for powered I.F.F. which seemed obvious enough to most of us, but the specification gave no recipe for the instrument to carry the idea into practice.

When instructed to undertake this work I put Carter on the job immediately. Carter had taken part in all I.F.F. work to date and was a very useful man with circuits and a fast and zealous worker. The problem was that a compact but fairly sensitive receiver would have to be used to receive the pulses from the Chain Stations and that the receiver pulse would have to trigger an oscillator working on the same frequency as the receiver signal and then emit a strong pulse for reception by the Chain. I decided that a super-regenerative receiver should be small and sensitive enough, although possibly tricky to make. When handing the job to Carter I gave him a circuit diagram of an instrument he might find useful. His subsequent work certainly used the super-regenerative receiver but everything else was of his own devising.

A special aircraft was allocated by the Air Ministry for this work, a Handley-Page Harrow monoplane bomber which was based at Martlesham

Handley-Page
Harrow I.

Heath.* Problems arose as to which kind of aerial to employ for I.F.F. but I remembered that during 1931, when assisting R. H. Barfield in D.F. tests on signals transmitted from Bristol Bulldog fighters, I noted the "Christmas Tree" effect of the wingtip to tailplane aerials and had wondered whether the aerials could be buried in the wings, or if we could use the metal girders in other aircraft. Now I was presented with the opportunity to try out this idea without having to go through official channels. It so happened that the tailplane of the Harrow was almost exactly half a wavelength long at the Bawdsey frequency (22.7 Mhz). I decided to regard the fuselage as tapped to a "half wave dipole" at a voltage node and therefore not likely to have much effect on the current on the tailplane, and so made connection to the dipole electrically by means of a Y-Tap.

Not surprisingly Carter experienced some trouble when he first took the

*The story of this R.A.F. Station is given in *Martlesham Heath* by Gordon Kinsey, published by Terence Dalton, 1975.

equipment into the air, but even if the set itself did not function properly there was evidence that the tail aerial was working correctly, evidenced by signals received at Bawdsey when Carter put the set into oscillation. He soon got his set working correctly and we were able to demonstrate it to Rowe's satisfaction. On one occasion when Carter was airborne in the Harrow and I was operating the R.D.F. and passing plots over the telephone to Operations Room at Fighter Command Headquarters, I discovered a visit was taking place by Admiral of the Fleet Lord Chatfield, then Minister for the Co-ordination of Defence. As good echoes were being received from Carter's Harrow I passed plots on to the Operations Room, stressing that this aircraft was identifying itself as friendly. This was the first time identified plots had been accepted at the Command Operations Room and the staff there saw to it that Lord Chatfield was made aware of the fact.

Carter was the first to make powered I.F.F. apparatus; Preist and Taylor made their apparatus work soon afterwards, but I cannot recall the details of their methods and did not witness any trials of it.

In the spring of 1938 I was joined by M. C. Williams, and at Rowe's request he was asked to adjudicate between the Carter and the Preist-Taylor sets. He recommended the further development of the Carter set and the abandonment of the other, and he then began development with a view to early production. Williams made one major addition to the set, the ability to re-transmit pulses of different widths. This facility was used to identify aircraft as fighter or coastal, etc., and there was a very wide pulse for distress purposes.

When Williams' work had progressed sufficiently a contractor, Ferranti, was brought in to produce a few sets to be used during the 1939 Air Exercises. Several of these sets were fitted to Avro Anson aircraft, the aerial being a copper tape fitted along the leading edge of the wooden tailplane. For the other aircraft taking part, Y-taps on the tailplanes would have been used. I cannot recall what results were obtained in the short period of use before the sets were hastily removed by the aircrews after fire had broken out in them. When Ferranti investigated the trouble it was discovered that the reservoir capacitors across the H.T. supply had become excessively hot due to conduction through their unsuitable dielectric.

These first Mark One sets were used by Coastal Command as they worked on the lower frequency, but Williams started on the development of the Mark Two set to cover the whole of the Chain frequencies (22-60 Mh.) and it was this set which was ultimately installed in thousands of aircraft during the war. Aerials for the latter sets on most aircraft were the Y-tap on the tailplane, and such an aerial was found to work well. In a few cases difficulty was experienced in obtaining a good enough aerial using the tailplane; the Bristol Blenheim and Blackburn Skua were examples of such cases, all of which were dealt with by using taps on the mainplane.

The prototype Avro Anson K.4771 undergoes maintenance in B Flight hangar at Martlesham Heath. Aircraft of this type were later involved in the development of I.F.F. and A.I. sets.

Flight

Sir Edward Appleton was made a member of the Tizard Committee when it was re-formed after the resignation of all of the original members in October, 1936. The only suggestion of a technical character he made which came to my knowledge was a circuit for I.F.F. His note on this was shown to me by Watson Watt during 1942, although it had obviously been written much earlier. I was asked if it contained anything of value. It was clearly too late to consider alternative circuits when thousands of I.F.F. sets were already in satisfactory use, unless Appleton's circuit had shown major advantages over the existing one, and this was not the case.

The Station moved to Dundee in Scotland at the outbreak of hostilities and then in May, 1940, it moved down to Swanage in Dorset. The Mark Three I.F.F. was in full development, but I played no further part in the programme, having been moved to new work at the Air Ministry.

This ends Mr Wilkins' account of the work on radar, which continued at Bawdsey after the research unit had departed from Suffolk. While it is possibly too technical in parts for some readers, it nevertheless presents a vivid picture of the frustrations and disappointments which accompanied the occasional joy of achievement experienced by those engaged in this new and exciting research.

CHAPTER FOUR

Before the Fray

BEFORE its purchase the site had also been inspected by Wimperis and Rowe, who had peeped through hedges and looked over walls and had obtained local knowledge from the proprietor of a ginger-beer stall sited near the Manor gate. The Tizard Committee recommended the purchase, which was then sanctioned by the Air Defence Sub-Committee of the Committee of Imperial Defence. Sir Phillip Cunliffe-Lister authorised the monetary aspect.

Spacious lawns, peach trees, bougainvillea bushes and the surrounding shingle and sand beaches made the site one of great beauty as well as of operational usefulness. Even the motto over the door — PLUTOT MOUVIR QUE CHANGER—FIRST IN THE FIELD — added to the air of the place.

Watson Watt set up his office in what is now the Ladies' Lounge of the Officers' Mess and the stable, coach-house and outbuildings were hastily transformed into workshops and laboratories. It had been decided from the onset that Bawdsey would not only operate as a research centre but would be the headquarters of the chain of R.D.F. air defence warning stations along the Southern North Sea and Channel coasts of the British Isles.

Working alongside the R.A.F. at the Manor was a team of War Office scientists. As a consequence of results which had been obtained at Orfordness the Army Council decided to be involved with research work along the lines of radio location for anti-aircraft gun sighting and later the problems involved with locating shipping from shore installations. The work of this team in using radio location to "spot" for coastal gun batteries resulted in, as a modified form, the Chain Home Low or C.H.L. system which enabled low-flying aircraft to be detected. The wavelength of 1.5 metres also made possible the development of smaller rotating aerials giving 360° coverage.

This group was later formed into the Air Defence Experimental Establishment, which in turn became the Ministry of Supply's Air Defence Research and Development Establishment under the leadership of Sir John Cockcroft, the distinguished physicist, and then the Radar Research and Development Establishment, firstly under the direction of Mr C. W. Oatley and then of Mr O. G. Sutton.

A wooden Chain Home receiver tower at Bawdsey, with the receiver hut at the base of the tower and the radar workshops visible at bottom left. *Mrs Sylvia Evans*

A great deal of work on radio location techniques for directing anti-aircraft guns had been carried out at Bawdsey and the first practical equipment had been devised by Mr P. E. Pollard during 1937; the first gun-laying radio location equipment (G.L.I.) went into service during the Spring of 1939. It was capable of a range of 10 miles with an accuracy of approximately 25 yards, but gave no angle of elevation. This was eventually rectified when a Cossor Limited engineer, Mr L. H. Bedford, designed an elevation finder, but as this relied on reflected pulses from the ground unlevel terrain gave a spurious reading; to overcome this an artificial ground level was established by stretching wire netting around the receiver as a level datum.

Radio location equipment was first used to control heavy guns in action on 1st October, 1940. Day tests had shown that it appeared efficient and was practicable, and a new system of gun control was introduced based on information provided from the radio location gunlaying (G.L.) site adjacent to

The ferry landing stage and the ferry itself provided an essential link for those who served at Bawdsey. *T. N. Briggs*

the batteries. Proof of the pudding was the fact that from 1st October, 1940, until 20th January, 1941, the guns brought down 70 raiders by night, four times as many as were shot down by the R.A.F. during the same period.

Good as the detection equipment was, it was inaccurate when the angle of sight exceeded 45 degrees, which resulted in a large blind spot where individual guns worked on sight of self-plotting principles. It was not until 1944 that new equipment came into operation capable of working at greater angles of sight and fitted with a tracking device which kept the sets automatically on target once it had been located. An innovation was the introduction of searchlight control and locator (S.C.L.), an electronic detector used in conjunction with searchlights which led to them being deployed in threes rather than simply as before.

Mr John Deller, of North Hykeham, near Lincoln, who was posted to Bawdsey Manor in January, 1937, and served there until joining the R.A.F. Educational Branch at Cranwell in September the next year, recalls that on arrival he was offered accommodation in the Manor but like so many others chose instead to live in Felixstowe. He remembers thoroughly enjoying the cycle ride each day to the ferry, which was operated by Charlie Brinkley, always identified by his metal hook hand.

He is by no means alone in remembering Charlie Brinkley, undoubtedly the best-known member of the Brinkley family, whose right hand had been replaced by a steel hook after an accident with an air-operated shotgun at his home on Havergate Island, near Orford. Everyone who ever served at Bawdsey seems to remember Charlie Brinkley with affection, and his hook somehow found its memorial in technical journals dealing with radar: when the electrical workshops at the Manor were devising an instrument to deal with an electronic problem they fashioned a device not unlike Charlie Brinkley's artificial "hand", and this became known officially in Royal Air Force instruction manuals as the Brinkley Hook.

Charlie Brinkley's son still runs the ferry, which has become something of a family tradition, and many a yachtsman has been relieved to see the Brinkleys' powerful motor boat coming to his aid when he has fallen foul of the treacherous bar at the mouth of the Deben. Salt is in the Brinkley blood, for there is no doubt that earlier members of the family had sailed the Seven Seas; it is recorded that a James Brinkley was hanged at Granville Point, Rhode Island, on 19th July, 1723, having been a member of the crew of the pirate ship *Ranger* commanded by a Captain Harris.

Mr Deller came to Bawdsey Manor as a junior member of a War Department (Army) team which was concerned with applying radio location methods to assist the scanning of searchlights. He recalls that the main depot was at Biggin Hill, Kent, and was under the direction of Dr E. T. Paris, later as Sir E. Talbot Paris to be Scientific Adviser to the Home Office, who during the 1914-18 war had perfected a sensitive hot-wire microphone for sound locators.

"Names which spring to mind in seniority order were Mr P. E. Pollard, a brilliant engineer and scientist, Captain Young, Mr Barber, and a local lad from Ipswich, Mr Kerridge. One unfortunate chap from the North-East, Mr Hunter Gray, was drowned one Saturday morning when the flying boat in which he was flying while carrying out experiments crashed off Bawdsey and all the crew perished. He and I walked together on many occasions in the evenings along Felixstowe promenade as far as the Dock just to 'spit in the sea'. We didn't have the money or the desire to spend much time in the local public house, and as a result maybe missed some of the local colour.

"Quite a few of the Bawdsey staff enjoyed playing Rugger with the Felixstowe team which performed on a ground just off the main road towards Trimley. One member who was a Manor resident, Dr Eddie Bowen, a Welsh exponent and a brilliant scientist, took us on many 'away' visits to other establishments. He later went to Australia and became an authority on radio astronomy. His work at Bawdsey involved a lot of flying from Martlesham Heath and I think greatly assisted in producing the later H2S equipment."

The difficulty of identifying friend and foe was not the only problem facing those early researchers. Mr Deller remembers that they also had difficulties with a tall water tower at the Royal Felixstowe Laundry at Walton, near Felixstowe, a place which should not be confused with Walton-on-the-Naze, whose jutting headland could be seen across Dovercourt Bay.

"The work at the Manor was a great mystery to the local populace and such things as verifying an echo from Walton water tower always needed diplomatic handling. For my part the work going on in other parts of the house and in the huts in the grounds was no great mystery. One met such people as Watson Watt, Wilkins, Bainbridge-Bell and Rowe over lunch or on the ferry, but the whole set-up was always hush-hush."

Another who remembers the early days at Bawdsey is Mr R. V. Perkins, of Malvern, whose first job after leaving the R.A.F. had just folded up, leading to a return to Ipswich for him and his wife.

"Having arrived back my next task was to find a job, but I also toyed with the idea of rejoining the R.A.F. as they were offering £100 for airmen to sign on because of the smell of a war in the offing. I was really reluctant to do this, so next morning I reported to the Labour Exchange, the first and only time in my life that I had been inside this sort of place. Little did I realise that this was to be the turning point of my life.

"I approached the desk and spoke to the clerk, who asked for details of my experience. When I had finished he took a card out from the rack and said, 'This might suit you. They're looking for craftsmen at the Air Ministry Research Station at Bawdsey.' I took the card and was directed to ask for Mr Airey, who was the Workshops Manager.

"My only mode of transport was a bicycle, so I rode the 16 miles from Ipswich and reached the beach at Bawdsey Ferry, where I asked how to get to the research station on the other side of the estuary. I was told that a boat would be across in a minute, and standing on the shingle beach I thought what a pretty place it was. It was just possible to see the towers of the Manor through the trees, and whilst I looked in that direction I saw a motor boat leaving the other side with the R.A.F. ensign flying from its stern. When it reached the Felixstowe Ferry shore I introduced myself to the boatman, a big red-faced happy-looking man named 'Tubby' Marjoram. This was to be only the first of many pleasant trips with him.

"The boatman took me across and explained that I would have to walk up a long drive and look for the stables, as these were now the workshops, and there I would find Mr Airey. It was a beautiful walk up the drive bordered by trees and shrubs of many kinds which blended into a magnificent pattern of colour. Eventually I reached the entrance to the stables, two towers supporting massive double doors which led on to a large courtyard surrounded by the stables, which were better built than a lot of houses I had seen. I inquired at the door for Mr Airey and was ushered into his office. He was a small man, most polite and sincere, and I liked him immediately. He told me he came from Lancashire and then asked me a whole lot of questions about my experience.

"He then said that he thought I was just the man he was looking for to be in charge of the machine shop which he was in the process of building up. We then took a tour of the Workshop, which was U-shaped and full of benches occupied by instrument makers. The machine shop was rather sparse, with a brand new Denham lathe and a small South Bend lathe. He told me that he was also getting a milling machine and asked me if I could operate one. There were two drilling machines and that was the lot.

"We returned to the office and talked terms. He told me that the rate for a machine operator was lower than that for an instrument maker, and noting the look on my face, then asked if I had any bench experience. On receiving an affirmative reply he said, 'So that settles that, you will be graded as an instrument maker, and also in charge of the machine shop'.

"The next step was to be vetted for security, and the usual procedure appeared to take some six weeks. I told him, 'That's not so good, as I've no job at the moment.' Mr Airey thought for a moment and then said, 'You were in the Air Force at Martlesham up to a few months ago, weren't you?'. I nodded. 'Hang on a moment,' he said, and put through a phone call to somebody. After speaking for a few minutes he put the phone down and said, 'That's O.K., son, you start on Monday.' I was delighted and thanked him. In all the years I worked in the Ministry I never heard of a quicker security clearance.

"Pushing the bike back to Ipswich at a fair rate of knots, I dashed in to tell my wife the good news. 'We will be getting 70 shillings a week', I announced, and after getting only £2 2s. a week plus rations in the R.A.F., it seemed like a fortune.

"It was in September, 1937, that I started at Bawdsey, and little did I realize that this was to be the start of 38 years' service. As we started at 7.45 a.m. I had to mount my bike in Ipswich at 6 a.m. but managed to get there on time, although the going was often extremely hard owing to the strong winds which seem to prevail along this part of the East Coast. The first day went off all right and the work didn't cause me any problems. The other chaps also seemed a decent lot.

"After we had clocked off we all walked down the drive from the workshop to the Ferry, where there were two motor launches which each carried about 12 people. One belonged to the Ministry and was piloted by 'Tubby' Marjoram, the other belonged to Charlie Brinkley, distinctive with his steel hook on his right arm. We had to get into the launches from the beach as there wasn't any landing stage either side of the river, so we often got our feet wet. We also had to leave our cycles on the Felixstowe side, and quite often when the tide came in extra high they got wet as well. After a day's work the ride home was very tiring, and it was nice to get the feet up after the 32-mile round trip.

"Thinking of alternative means of getting to work, I was talking to one of the chaps one morning about getting a house in Felixstowe and he said that he was leaving in a week's time and had a house in Looe Road, Felixstowe, and, would you believe it, the house belonged to Charlie Brinkley. I approached Charlie and offered to take the house over when the other chap left, and Charlie agreed. My wife was delighted as it was in a quiet road near Brackenbury Fort and only 1½ miles from Bawdsey Ferry. There was a large garden and the rent was 16s. 8d. per week, a fair sum in those days.

"I soon settled down at work and got to know all the chaps and Bosses. After a few weeks an Assistant Workshops Officer, Mr J. H. Morley, arrived. Next in line was the Workshop Foreman, Alf Bullard, who was very tool conscious; he had to be because the tool stores were pathetic! There was only one set of drills and one set of taps, and these had to be used on all types of materials, so you can imagine what sort of condition they were in.

"Many of the characters in the workshops became the nucleus of a team of skilled men who worked on radar, many of them carrying on right through the war and afterwards. In the instrument shop there was a little 'clique' comprising Bill Betts, Jack Trehearne and 'Dibber' Young, who were all famous for their practical jokes; then there was Jack Sibbet, an ex-R.A.F. chap who brought in lovely fresh doughnuts each day as he was married to a baker's daughter. The old originals were Wally Betteridge and Ted Seabrooke, as they had started with Alf Bullard at Slough Research Station. Others in the shop were Chris Hopper, Ben Brookes, Alf Grainger and 'Gracie' Williams, as well as Tommy Watson who was a real cricket fanatic.

"An amusing incident arose involving two chaps in which a bet was made regarding who would win a darts match which was to be held in the canteen during the lunch hour. The word got round and the place was crowded. One chap was favourite because he reckoned that he had been champion of the Sergeants' Mess when he was in the service, whereas the other was an absolute 'rabbit'. Some said that he had never seen a dart board, and coupled with this he was terribly short-sighted, wearing spectacles with thick lenses which made him look like an owl.

The Chain Home aerial towers rise above the trees at Bawdsey, the shorter wooden receiver towers standing out somewhat starkly against the slimmer steel transmitter towers. The steel piling at the river mouth was put in place to counteract severe scouring caused by the tidal currents.   *Mrs M. Beck*

Looking down on the stables and courtyard, with the Mess Hall in the bottom left-hand corner. The Chain Home School billet is the building with the ventilated roof and the Fire Section and Motor Transport crewroom were housed in the dark hut.   *Mrs Sylvia Evans*

"The match was an absolute scream. The 'rabbit' had to be told how to start and finish on a double and the spectators even had to show him the numbers that he wanted. To everyone's surprise he won the first leg — he had an amazing 'eye' and had only to be shown the number required in order to put a dart in it. The favourite was furious and promptly doubled the stakes, then he evened things up by winning the second leg. His opponent was a born comedian and kept cracking jokes and taunting him, which put him off his game, and he became more and more erratic so that he lost the final leg and the bet!

"At that time there were about twenty chaps in the workshops, and rumours of an impending war made our work vitally important. Due to the increasing work load new arrivals came almost weekly and among these were Dilutees, which meant that they were unskilled but had received some training at a Government Centre. Two such men were

'Tich' Date and Joe Payne. Skilled men who joined us were Bert Brogden, Jack Mather, Les Morrel, Charlie Parkhurst and Fred Loades, whose hobby was producing miniature fairgrounds, which he does to this very day at Westerfield, near Ipswich.

"During those days it was quite usual for the scientific staff to visit the workshops to get jobs done and explain what they wanted. One of these was Bainbridge-Bell, a nice old chap with snowy white hair; he always wore his trousers at 'half-mast'. Of course this tickled 'Gracie', who would prance up and down the shop with his trousers pulled up to his knees.

"Football was played during the lunch-hour with a scratch team composed of all sides of the Establishment. I was elected captain. We played some friendly matches against the local teams at the weekends, including Martlesham Heath, my old team. Among the team were Charlie Peachey and Les Boram from Admin, Wally Betteridge and myself from the workshops, Dr Whelpton and B. Woods from the scientists, and Corporal White and L.A.C. Suggett from the R.A.F.

"Part of the workshops set-up was a team of riggers whose function was to erect the transmitting towers all over the country. Bert Goldsmith was in charge of this team, and what a lad he was; he knew all the 'dodges'. One scientist who worked on the towers with them was Alec Muir, a tall slim chap. I mustn't forget Jimmy Rowe, who was Dr Watson Watt's secretary and chief administrator; he eventually became Director, a job which he fulfilled during the whole of the war. A chap named Arthur Wolleter was his 'eyes and ears', as nothing happened on the Station that Arthur didn't know about, and of course it found its way to Jimmy's ears. 'Chiefy' Francis was Jimmy's general factotum and odd job man; he was an old sailor who lived in Bawdsey village — I've never heard a man who could swear like him."

The Air Estimates for 1937 allotted £100,000 for an unspecified site in East Anglia. One can only assume that the amenities to be provided by this expenditure must have been at Bawdsey. Then on 8th June, 1938, Mr Stanley Baldwin became Prime Minister and Sir Phillip Cunliffe-Lister, who had earlier authorised expenditure on the purchase of Bawdsey Manor, and later to be raised to the peerage as Lord Swinton, succeeded Lord Londonderry as Minister for Air. Before long the moves that were being made resulted in the formation of the Committee of Imperial Defence on Air Defence Research.

Before long a difference of opinion arose on this committee, as its members felt that Professor Lindemann, one of the committee members, was too close to Mr Winston Churchill, who did not at that time hold Government office, and was likely to reveal to him some of the top-secret matters discussed by the committee. The other members appeared to feel that Sir Henry Tizard, who was then Rector of the Imperial College of Science and Technology, London, should be the prime voice for the committee, and as a result of pressure being brought to bear on him Lindemann resigned. He was, however, reinstated later in the year.

Events connected with the development of R.D.F. moved fast after the formation of the Technical Committee for Air Defence Communications under the chairmanship of Mr O. Anson, of the G.P.O. Among the members of this sub-committee of the Air Defence Communications Committee were several men who over the years were to become household names, including Air Vice-Marshal Sir Philip Joubert de la Ferté, Mr Robert Watson Watt, Air Marshal Sir Hugh Dowding, later to be head of Fighter Command during the Battle of Britain, and Air Commodore Warrington-Morris.

Squadron Leader R. G. Hart, later Air Marshal Sir Raymond Hart, arrived at the Manor as its first technical officer and in January, 1937, established a training school. Other early arrivals were Flight Sergeant W. G. Lawrence, later to reach the rank of wing commander, and Flight Sergeant Scarff Webb, who were posted to Bawdsey for R.D.F. training. A few years

A view of the courtyard from one of the receiver towers. The MT bays are on the left, the crewrooms in the middle and the fire hut at bottom centre. *Mrs Sylvia Evans*

later Wing Commander Lawrence opened the operational R.D.F. station at Dover.

During May, 1937, a Chain Home station built at the Manor was handed over to the Royal Air Force, and Bawdsey began its life as an operational station on 24th September that year. That station, the world's first radio location unit, was followed by two others during July and August, but the use of three operational stations created problems in sorting out sightings, these problems being amplified by small errors of calibration, by operator error and by aerials which sometimes "played up". In order to sort out the information coming from the stations Squadron Leader Hart commissioned an experimental filter room during August, 1937, and this assisted materially in identifying aircraft sightings.

Tremendous efforts were being made to get the new equipment airborne, but this did not prevent members of both the R.A.F. and civilian staff from enjoying some moments of relaxation. Wing Commander H. J. Sanders, who was serving at Martlesham Heath in 1936, remembers some of these moments:

"We often bathed just around the Point, and when Bawdsey was taken over one of our Equipment Officers, 'Dolly' Doyle, had charge of the inventory. The Manor having its own private beach, I suggested that we made this into a Mess Bathing Site Club. Plenty of room for car parking and places to take our wives for picnics, but No, No, No!—far too hush-hush for any of that."

Mr Perkins, too, remembers the attractions of Bawdsey Manor.

"The Manor was surrounded by beautiful gardens which in the summer were a riot of glorious colour. There was a fantastic lily-pond full of beautiful goldfish and ornamental plants. We used to stroll in the gardens during the lunch hour, and one day a few of us were there when we bumped into 'Chiefy' Francis, who said 'Follow me, and don't make a noise!' He took us down a narrow path through some bushes to the edge of the cliff, where he waved us down, and we crept on our hands and knees to the brink. What a sight greeted us! We were looking down on three young ladies, sunbathing completely nude. They were in a very secluded spot, and unaware that they could be seen, and so we silently stole away.

"On fine days we would go for a swim, and most of the staff were there, including Jimmy Rowe and his wife."

Wing Commander Sanders recalls that Mr Watson Watt and some of his scientists often visited his Instrument Section at Martlesham Heath to see if any of his testing equipment could be used in their experiments. Some of the Martlesham aircraft were fitted up for their express requirements, one of the first aircraft employed in this work being Avro Anson K.6260, which resembled a porcupine with aerials protruding through the cabin windows and roof. Other aircraft used in the Bawdsey experiments and belonging to the Aircraft Experimental Co-operation Unit or D Flight were Avro Anson K.8758, Fairey Battles K.9207, K.9208 and K9230, the all-wooden Miles Magister L.8168, de Havilland D.H.60M Moth K.1876, and Handley-Page Harrow K.7021.

Convincing results were obtained during 1937 when Anson K.6260 managed to locate, through cloud, two capital ships of the Home Fleet, the battleship H.M.S. *Rodney* and the aircraft carrier H.M.S. *Courageous*, as they steamed along the East Coast on their way to the North of Scotland. As this was a "blind fix" it proved that the new equipment had potential. The intensity of the work carried out by these aircraft is revealed in the Aircraft Utilisation Log for three months in early 1938 when they spent 94 hours airborne, an exceptional amount considering the "down time" necessary for fitting equipment. The success of this work was even more remarkable as at any one time there were no more than twelve Bawdsey men engaged on this task.

Several of the large flying boats from the Marine Aircraft Experimental Establishment (M.A.E.E.) at Felixstowe also co-operated in this work. As recorded previously, one crashed while carrying out an experiment, with the loss of all on board. Another tragedy took place within sight of the Manor when a Miles Magister two-seat light training monoplane, on test from Martlesham Heath, was carrying out spinning trials over the mouth of the River Deben. When it failed to recover from one such manoeuvre, the pilot, Flight Lieutenant Simmonds, baled out and alighted in the sea. Several people witnessed the incident and it was thought that the pilot had been rescued by a passing paddle steamer, but unfortunately this was not the case. His body with his parachute still attached was brought ashore by a local fisherman a few days later. One of the pilots engaged in the search for the missing airman was Flight Lieutenant Ramsbottom-Isherwood, who later during the Second World War commanded an R.A.F. Hurricane wing in Russia and was killed post-war flying a Gloster Meteor jet fighter which crashed in a snowstorm while flying from East Anglia to Kent.

During 1937 Watson Watt put forward his theory that women would make better R.D.F. operators than men, and in order to prove this statement he trained three shorthand typists who worked at the Station in this new work. The ladies proved extremely efficient and as a result further women were trained, thus forming the vanguard of the thousands who were later engaged in this work. Miss Parry, later Mrs Girdlestone, who had worked as a cashier in a Felixstowe butcher's shop, was one of the original three lady plotters; eventually she carried out special plotting duties at Fighter Command Headquarters.

Dr R. V. Jones, later Professor and Head of British Scientific Intelligence, visited the Manor during June, 1937, in order to become acquainted with the infant development of the new weapon. He returned later in the year and witnessed further new work in the R.D.F. Development Section, which was under the leadership of Mr E. G. Bowen and numbered among its members Mr Gerald Torch and Mr R. Hanbury-Brown.

At the time of the Munich Crisis much thought was given to the defence of the Establishment should hostilities break out and plans were made for any such eventuality. Mr B. G. Goldsmith, B.E.M., of Kesgrave, recalls those days of uncertainty:

"The new C.H. stations were reaching out to the North East of England but at this time their coverage was somewhat sparse, and as a precaution emergency equipment was moved in to cover the blind spots. As a civilian

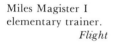

Miles Magister I elementary trainer.
Flight

aerial rigger I was ordered to make for the North at great speed with a lorry load of urgent equipment, driving non-stop through the night in a Merryweather truck which was towing a trailer, eventually arriving very tired at Drove Hill, near Eyemouth, Northumberland. There was no rest here, as the 70-foot mobile mast had to be erected. After all this effort the aerial was found to be unsuccessful and so we packed it all up again and came home at a more leisurely pace."

It is reported that Watson Watt went to Germany "on holiday" once or twice during this period, and reports show that the pioneer scientist and his wife went off to that country as amateur sleuths in the hope of discovering whether the Nazis were making pre-war radio-location experiments.

Information, although scant, had reached the British radio-location team during 1937 of a place in East Prussia which looked oddly like their own laboratories and of a curious new radio tower at Trier. So Robert Watson Watt and his wife assumed the role of tourists and made for the oddly named Gross Britannien, near Trier, in East Prussia. The guest house there was full, so the hostess said, so the tourists went to Neu Kirchen and stayed there for a

The German airship *Graf Zeppelin* over the Suffolk coast in 1939 when seeking information on the Bawdsey transmissions.   *Mr G. Soar*

walking and bus tour of the district. They had a particular interest in church steeples which commanded a good view of radio and high tension electric towers.

They interviewed one of Hermann Goering's gamekeepers who had the pleasantest recollections of being a prisoner of war in England during 1917, and also read the archives of Elburg recording the close ties between that part and Dundee, their old home. But their efforts were rewarded with the discovery of no more than a broadcasting station or two and a few high tension lines; they found no sign of any radio location research.

If their "holiday" had been successful it could have offset to some extent the number of "artists and bird-watchers" who frequented the Bawdsey peninsular during those pre-war Summer days. The secret was, however, capable of protection, as the Manor was situated on a triangular headland with the sea on one side, the river on the other and only one road leading from the landward side to the Station. Pre-war motorists in the area recall "authentic rumours", never first hand but always from reliable sources, of cars whose engines for some unaccountable reason refused to function in spite of every effort on the part of their drivers to rectify faults. The usual story was that an R.A.F. officer or senior N.C.O. would come along the road and ask if the motorist was in trouble and, on receiving the usual answer, would inform the perplexed driver that at such and such a time all would be restored to working order. As in all such stories, this is just what happened; and so the story spread far and wide that the tall towers at Bawdsey could inhibit the ignition of car engines. Cover story or not, it worked, and many people were convinced of its effectiveness. A smaller school of thought promoted the "Death Ray" theory; little did they know of the experiments in this field at Orfordness detailed in *Orfordness — Secret Site*, which also tells of the early development of radar.

Whatever the conjectures and the rumours at home in Suffolk, the "opposition" were now extremely inquisitive regarding the tall steel and wooden masts which rose from the several sites around the East and South coasts. As a result the German airship *Graf Zeppelin* was recommissioned under the direction of General Martini, Director General of Signals for the Luftwaffe. Specialised detection equipment was installed and the airship cruised slowly up and down the North Sea in an attempt to detect transmissions from these new sites. The attempt failed, but had the airship's detection apparatus been more efficient the *Graf Zeppelin* ought certainly to have been able to carry back to her masters the information that the R.A.F. had a radio location system working.

Bawdsey continued transmissions throughout the cruise and from the snooper's signals back to her base was able to divine her intentions. Indeed on one occasion when she repeatedly requested navigational information from her base, this could have been easily supplied by Bawdsey!

The pulses from the British detection system can have been no surprise to the "snoopers" as Germany had in being at that time a technically efficient detection system, thought by many to have been on a par with the British efforts. The difference was that at Bawdsey the practical side had been more efficiently developed and integrated into a working air defence medium, thus making Great Britain the world leader.

When a delegation from the Luftwaffe led by Generals Erhard Milch and Ernst Udet paid a visit to the Royal Air Force in October, 1937, their tour included a visit to the newly commissioned bomber station at Mildenhall, Suffolk. Milch, in conversation in the Officers' Mess at Fighter Command Headquarters on their return from that visit to Suffolk, surprised the assembled company of officers with the question "How are you getting on with your experiments in the detection by radio of aircraft approaching your shores?" After the embarrassed chatter had died down Milch continued, "We have known for some time that you were developing a system of radio detection, and so are we, and we think we are ahead of you!"

It is now known that Milch was correct to a point, as Dr Rudolf Kühnhold, the Chief of the German Navy's Signals Research Unit, had indeed built a practical radio location set during 1934, and by the outbreak of hostilities Germany had defence and gun-laying radio location equal to the British. It was, however, in the further development and practical application that Germany failed, the work which had been initiated at Orfordness and had grown to fruition at Bawdsey forging ahead and overtaking that of the Germans.

After hostilities commenced Germany failed again in that she did not destroy the vital detecting stations. America was later to regret not having investigated the new weapon sooner, feeling that in her geographical position there was no need for a detection system. France had developed a radio navigational system for her crack transatlantic liner, the *Normandie*, but it was purely a civil application.

It may come as a surprise to many readers that during the late 1930s great Britain had a good lead on the rest of the world in television development and that over 20,000 receiver sets were licensed at that time. This service was of course shut down at the outbreak of war.

When R.A.F. personnel were posted to Bawdsey for training they were billeted for a while at the R.A.F. station at Felixstowe,* from where they travelled to the Manor each day, in civilian clothes, so security minded were the administrators of the new project. Several of the early Women's Auxilary Air Force (W.A.A.F.) R.D.F. operators who attended the initial courses remembered their days at Bawdsey and their billets in the nearby Coastguard cottages on the cliff overlooking the North Sea. A fine personal narrative of those days by Daphne Griffiths, later Flight Officer Garne, is to be found in her book *The Eyes of the Few*, published by Macmillan.

One of the early trainees at Bawdsey was a young Flight Sergeant at Hornchurch, a fighter station in Essex, who found himself posted "out of the blue" to R.A.F. Felixstowe in the Winter of 1938. Ten years later, as Wing Commander Kenneth Mummery, he was to return to Bawdsey as commanding officer. He recalls his reaction to the sudden posting:

"As I had just met a young lady who was later to become my wife, I was not greatly pleased at the move. However, consoled by my colleagues with the usual service morale booster of 'You shouldn't have joined', I packed and reported at Felixstowe. On arrival at that station, the Orderly Room Sergeant informed me I was for 'that place across the river' and transport would take me there in the morning, together with five other new arrivals. It did, as far as the River Deben at Felixstowe Ferry, where a one-armed boatman took us across in his stout motor-boat.

*The story of this staion is given in *Seaplanes — Felixstowe* by Gordon Kinsey, published by Terence Dalton, 1978.

"Bawdsey Manor was peopled by busy young civilians — we six new arrivals, all wireless Flight Sergeants, were the only uniformed people in sight. In the classroom we were addressed by Squadron Leader Tester, who was wearing 'mufti', as indeed we would be required to do after this lecture, he informed us. This was one of the security rules.

"Squadron Leader Tester amazed us with his first introduction to Radio Locating and Direction Finding. Just reflect on the situation, as it presented itself to six young airmen in November, 1938. Munich was recently over, the country was thoroughly alarmed at our vulnerability to a belligerent and bellicose Germany because of the R.A.F.'s numerical inferiority. We were told of a discovery that would make us aware of the presence of aircraft and their location by night and day, in fog or clear, and we had been picked to run the first of six such stations being erected around the coastline. My colleagues, Swinney, Rowe, Strevons, Lawrence, Emeny and myself were all concentrated attention. Here we were required to play a part in redressing the numerical handicap under which the R.A.F., if it went to war, would inevitably suffer. We would send our fighters just where they were required and use them to the best advantage.

"We had a busy six weeks of concentrated study at Bawdsey and burned the midnight oil at our homework, mastering new techniques. Occasionally we went for a drink at the Alderton village public house, where a mobile fish and chip shop would stop on certain evenings to dispense delectable hot suppers. Emblazoned on its sides was the motto 'Cleanliness with Civility', while the coal-fired cooker belched forth clouds of thick yellow smoke into the village street!

"After our hectic six weeks we dispersed to our several stations, Stoke Holy Cross, Darsham High Street, Dover, Dunkirk, Pevensey and Poling, which we soon put on the air and which were to play such an important part in the Battle of Britain.

"Operating within No. 60 (Signals) Group, the new stations did their best to remain operational, but many difficulties were encountered during these early days. Not the least of these difficulties was the fact that as the new equipment was quite unlike anything else that had been previously produced, spares were few and far between. Indeed, the movement of spares from the manufacturers was so rapid that there was no time for part identification numbers and usually it was left to mechanics in the know to send the correct item and for their counterparts at the out-stations to identify them when received."

Five R.D.F. stations, including Bawdsey and Great Bromley, were operating during the 1938 Annual Home Defence Exercises in August of that year, and operators at these stations were able to watch Mr Neville

47

Chamberlain's Lockheed airliner as it flew to Munich for his appointment with Hitler.

Several problems were encountered, the most important being the obscure "blips" which were received by the rear faces of the aerials and which gave a false impression of activity. Later on this phenomenon was to feature in the so-called "Battle of Barking Creek" on 3rd September, 1939, when the defences were in a sensitive state. A plot made by the local R.D.F. was reported to North Weald Sector Operations, who then transmitted it to Headquarters, No. 18 Observer Group at Colchester. R.A.F. North Weald despatched eighteen Hawker Hurricanes to the scene of the plot, a point near

Hawker Hurricane I of the type which entered service before the war, with two-bladed Watts wooden airscrew and fabric-covered mainplanes.

the Thames Estuary. Sirens sounded and the Navy brought their high-angle anti-aircraft guns into action, while the fighters wheeled around each other in the cloud-flecked skies. The pilots, fearing the worst, took shots at aircraft as they appeared from out of the clouds, with the result that the second section of fighters intercepted the first section.

Police at Mistley, Essex, reported a bullet-holed Hurricane down in their district while another one came down in the same vicinity. After the confusion the remainder returned home somewhat red-faced. It was quickly realised that urgent steps would have to be taken to eliminate the obscure plot obtained from the rear face of the aerial.

Mr J. Dodman, of Ipswich, was driving a lorry in the vicinity of the encounter and to his amazement observed a Hurricane make a somewhat bumpy but safe landing in a field. Stopping his vehicle, he grabbed the lorry's fire extinguisher from its bracket and ran over to the aircraft, from which a dazed pilot was climbing down. When he had collected his wits, the pilot told Mr Dodman that he was sure that he had been shot at by a Hurricane but could not at the time believe it to be so.

Air Vice-Marshal C. H. N. Bilney, who was at Martlesham Heath at this time, recalls:

"At about 8.30 one morning a pilot arrived at the camp and said that he had been shot down just outside Ipswich. I collected our Civil Engineering Officer, Mr Roworth, and away we went to the scene of the forced landing. Talking to the pilot who had been flying the aircraft, he said that he thought, but was not wholly sure, that it was a Hurricane that had shot him down. On arrival at the downed Hurricane we found the radiator holed, as well as a number of hits on the wings.

"Knowing that German bullets had steel cores as opposed to the lead cores of ours, I got a piece of wood, put some glue on one end and fished around in the wing for bullet fragments. I soon found quite a lot of lead, so the pilot's suspicions were confirmed."

As a result of this episode a fresh reporting procedure was brought into force as an urgent measure in order to eliminate any recurrence of this incident. To back up the new measures, the Observer Corps was strengthened and the long-serving No. 18 Group at Colchester divided and joined with a section of No. 16 Group, Norwich, in order to form a mid-section Group at Bury St Edmunds, No. 14 Group.

In order that the new radio location system could be used to its greatest advantage, a complementary organisation was set up at R.A.F. Biggin Hill, Kent. The man behind this was Henry Tizard, who saw that the infant radio location chain was already making the R.A.F. Fighter Command's defence tactics outdated and that completely new methods of placing fighters in the air were required.

At Biggin Hill Dr B. G. Dickins came to the conclusion that radio location would be capable of detecting aircraft flying at 1,000 feet at distances of up to 50 miles. In order to ascertain practical working figures aircraft were sent out over the sea and then directed to approach the coast from distances of 50 miles. These machines were equipped with radio sets which transmitted radio signals to simulate radio location echoes, these signals being picked up by the then standard radio direction receivers so that it was possible to plot the "invading" aircraft. The results were analysed and it was found that existing interception schemes were deficient; new controlling and direction techniques had to be evolved.

It may seem strange that as a result of this work at Biggin Hill, Royal Air Force fighter pilots were being trained in radio location assisted interception before the device itself had been developed. Without this training Fighter Command would have been in dire straits during the Battle of Britain, as otherwise there would have been no time to train the pilots before the action began.

Another factor which contributed in no small way to the outcome of the Battle was training received by fighter pilots in an "unorthodox exercise". After January, 1938, R.A.F. fighter pilots directed by Biggin Hill indulged in concealed mock attacks on all civil airliners approaching the British Isles. As these aircraft were usually making for the pre-war London Air Terminal at Croydon, their tracks were roughly in line with that of an aircraft on course for the capital city. Observations were also made by the new equipment installed at Bawdsey, and from the data received and collected the Operations Room at Biggin Hill was able to evolve the system of day fighter control used to such good effect in the days to come.

Defence problems connected with the Bawdsey site were tested during January, 1939, when Bristol Blenheim bombers of No. 104 Squadron based at Bassingbourn made dummy attacks on the station. They were able to achieve partial penetration by flying extremely low under the detecting screen.

On the day that Mussolini invaded Albania, Good Friday, 1939, fifteen Chain Home Stations went on the air as the vanguard of the new defence system. During June, Mr Winston Churchill in his capacity as a member of the Air Defence Research Committee flew to Martlesham Heath with Sir Henry Tizard and was taken to Bawdsey to see the progress that had been made. This was a return home for Sir Henry, as he had been the first Scientific Officer at Martlesham Heath when it had been established during January, 1917. The visit is recorded in Sir Robert Watson-Watt's book, *Three Steps to Victory*.

The Chain Home transmitter aerial towers march in line along the cliff top, displaying their seemingly slender construction, while the wooden receiver towers can be seen in the background.

Churchill's report stated that he found the unit profoundly interesting and also encouraging. He also observed that in his estimation the site would need immediate protection and also that as the station at this time was "forward looking" only, observation behind the station was still in the hands of the Observer Corps. This visit was followed by one from Sir Hugh Dowding during June. On this occasion he flew from Martlesham Heath in a Fairey Battle equipped with an early Air Interception set to see for himself how the new device worked.

Plotting took considerable time and did not yet conform with Fighter Command's Standard Grid System. This difficulty was overcome by one of the Bawdsey staff, Mr G. A. Roberts, who, using automatic telephone methods, evolved an electrical convertor device which became known as the "Fruit Machine". This conveyed observation data direct to R.A.F. Control Head-quarters by means of keys which were depressed by the operators.

Mr Robert Watson Watt was promoted from Superintendent at Bawdsey to Head of the Directorate of Communications Development at the Air Ministry in April, 1938, Mr A. P. Rowe becoming Superintendent at the Manor. Henceforth Mr L. S. Harley served as the link-man between the Bawdsey Research Station and Watson Watt's department at the Air Ministry. Mr Harley, who described himself as "the Man from the Ministry", says he had little direct contact with individuals at Bawdsey other than A. P. Rowe, of whom he says:

"Although he was insistent on discipline to an extent unpopular with the many individualists among the scientific staff, we got on well together and used to visit the Star public house in Bawdsey village, where he introduced me to that delightful Irish fantasy 'The Crock of Gold' by James Stephens."

Another of the scientific officers serving at Bawdsey in the pre-war years was Mr J. H. Phillips, B.Sc., A.M.I.E.E., F.P.S., who twenty years later became Director of the Air Ministry's Guided Weapons Techniques Department.

In spite of the work of the War Office team at Bawdsey in the late 1930s radio location sets for directing anti-aircraft guns were not due to be delivered until 1940, so with the war clouds visibly gathering sound locators, with all their many limitations, were adapted to track night raiders. For the defence of London these locators were sited according to the Fixed Azimuth System, with two lines of sound locators spaced at two-mile intervals on the Eastern flank of the capital at right angles to the Thames. Each locator was linked with the London Gun Operations Room, from which information on angles of sight, bearings, direction and speed was passed to the anti-aircraft batteries.

At the outbreak of war the East Coast of Britain was protected by an electronic curtain capable of detecting aircraft at heights of up to 15,000 feet and at ranges of more than 100 miles irrespective of weather conditions. Cloud, rain, light and dark made no difference to the all-seeing eye of the Chain Home (C.H.) stations as they carried on their endless vigil. Besides giving knowledge of the raiders' approach, development was such that their numbers could be counted and any moves that they made from their original course could be watched and countered. The Chain Home stations used wavelengths of about 10 metres, the signals being emitted in pulses from the 360-foot aerial towers, and the echoes returned to the wooden receiver aerial towers were visibly displayed on a cathode ray tube.

Good as this C.H. system was, the 10 metre waves were not able to detect objects in the lower sphere of operations and low flying aircraft were still able to approach undetected. In order to combat this deficiency another system known as Chain Home Low (C.H.L.) was evolved, the initial work being done by Mr W. A. S. Butement.

The main difference between the two systems was that while Chain Home was a forward looking system, Chain Home Low, using 1½ metre waves as the result of newly developed radio valves, was able due to the shorter wavelengths to utilise a much smaller aerial system mounted on a rotating mounting. Instead of being forward looking, the new system now scanned the whole 360° horizon lower down and low-flying aircraft were detected by their maximum intensity of returned echoes.

Wing Commander Kenneth Mummery remembers that the new system had its drawbacks as well as its advantages:

"Several mechanical problems were encountered during the early days of C.H.L. stations, as the narrower beam aerial array had to be rotated in order to sweep or scan, and many novel methods were devised to obtain this movement. One remembered by many was a framework not unlike that of a bicylce frame, with handlebars and seat, chainwheel and pedals which, when they were turned, rotated the aerial through a series of gears and links. A joke enjoyed by the 'informed' was that one could always identify one of the W.A.A.F. R.D.F. operators by her bulging calf muscles and unusually slim figure."

Quite apart from the mechanical problems, operators at C.H.L. stations were also plagued by the spurious echoes produced by large flocks of seabirds. Although of low signal strength, they were tracked at the same speed as small fast vessels, but the operators soon learnt to detect the difference between the true and the false echoes.

Nevertheless, migrating geese, clearly unaware of wartime flight restrictions, caused some anxious moments to the men and women of the C.H.L. stations. So did large flocks of starlings during those wartime autumns.

CHAPTER FIVE

War work

Oɴ THE outbreak of hostilities on 3rd September, 1939, it was realised that Bawdsey was in too exposed a position to be home to a team engaged in highly important research work, so the Bawdsey Research Station packed its several bags.

"A couple of days before war was declared we were told to get ready for complete evacuation," recalls Mr R. V. Perkins. "Everybody was detailed to stay at work packing up, so we sent messages to our wives not to expect us home. My job was to see that all the machines and tools were packed, and we experienced quite a deal of trouble getting the machines on to the lorries — all we had were ropes and rollers. The machines had to be man-handled up a four-foot ramp on to the lorries, a very tricky operation. After we had loaded our goods and chattels we assisted the scientific staff to pack, and eventually we made our farewells to the place that we had grown to love over the last few years."

One group moved to Christchurch, in Hampshire; another headed by Dewhurst made for Leighton Buzzard in Bedfordshire, where it became the nucleus of No. 60 Group; Larnder took his group to Stanmore in Middlesex; others joined Watson Watt at Fighter Command Headquarters, also at Stanmore; some made the long journey to Dundee, where the Telecommunications Research Establishment was set up, and the airborne research section went to the aerodrome at Perth, some twenty miles from the main group. Some members of the civilian staff were asked to move to Worth Matravers, in Dorset, a few months later. Last to leave were Mr Airey, who was in charge of the workshops, and Mr Sopwith, in charge of stores.

A flight sergeant and twelve airmen also left Bawdsey to form a Mobile Radio Location Unit for service with the British Expeditionary Force in France.

Not all those who had been engaged in development work at Bawdsey went with their colleagues to new locations. Mr William Cusack Fahie was commissioned into the R.A.F.V.R. on the outbreak of war and was posted overseas, serving in the Middle East until returning to the United Kingdom in 1943 to become Deputy Chief Signals Plans for the 9th United States Air Force for the Normandy invasion. Later he became Chief Signals Plan and

Operations to the Airborne Forces, with the rank of Wing Commander, and after the war he was managing director of Reavell-Fahie Limited, of Ipswich.

During the pre-war period a great deal of work had been carried out on Air Interception equipment by Mr E. G. Bowen, who had been one of the original Orfordness staff and had moved to Bawdsey, assisted by Dr W. B. Lewis. They were instrumental in solving many of the initial problems, and such was their progress that by 1940 the airborne set was able to detect and indicate the position of an aircraft flying in front of the aeroplane in which it was installed, making possible a stern attack on an enemy aircraft in darkness.

Just before the outbreak of war early Mark I Air Interception sets had been installed in the twin-engined night fighter version of the Bristol Blenheim Mk. I flown by No. 25 Squadron from Martlesham Heath. When the Aeroplane and Armament Experimental Establishment moved from Martlesham Heath to Boscombe Down, in Wiltshire, and with it the Special Duties Flight and the aircraft used for airborne test work, No. 25 Squadron moved to Perth, though the Squadron's Radio Location Flight soon returned south to St Athan in South Wales, moving from there to Worth Matravers. Early in 1940 some of the Flight filtered back to Martlesham Heath and operations were carried out from that airfield by Blenheims of what became known as the Bawdsey Flight. These combined tracking of Luftwaffe mine-laying floatplanes and flying boats making their nightly expeditions to the sea lanes off the East Anglian coast with the calibration of the East Coast Chain Home stations.

Work done at Bawdsey on the development of airborne radar was ably backed up by many scientists and their teams of research workers in other places. Among them were Dr E. L. C. White and Mr A. D. Blumlein of Electrical Musical Industries (E.M.I.), the research staff of A. C. Cossor Limited, Dr C. C. Paterson and the General Electric Company team, and the staff of Pye Limited and E. K. Cole Limited, the latter being responsible for the manufacture of the earliest successful airborne sets.

For some time the research staff at Bawdsey had envisaged that development of microwaves was imperative for more effective operation, but at this time there was no valve capable of generating the very high power necessary for this purpose. The breakthrough came during the early months of 1940 when Professor Randall, later Sir John Randall, and a team of scientists at Birmingham University devised the Magnetron, a wonder power unit no larger than a small orange, yet able to generate an output of hundreds of kilowatts in short pulses.

Later in the year, and some sixteen months before America entered the war, a delegation of scientists under the title of the Tizard Mission took Britain's latest scientific discoveries to the United States; the Magnetron was among them. With the aid of this British invention the Americans were able to forge ahead with the development of air and surface interception and AA gun control radar.

An R.A.F. officer who remembers this period well is Wing Commander John R. Turnbull, who was at Bawdsey for rather more than a year. He recalls his posting to Bawdsey Manor as Equipment Officer in October, 1939, just after the experimental station staff had all left for their various destinations:

"On our arrival my wife and I stayed in the village at the Red House as paying guests for two months. Thereafter I rented a picturesque thatched cottage in Links Avenue, Felixstowe, right opposite the entrance to the

Bristol Blenheim I twin-engined bomber converted to a heavy night fighter and carrying the first examples of Air Interception sets. The wartime censor has removed the aerials from the starboard wing and nose while leaving the one under the port wing.

British Aircraft Corporation

Golf Club. The Station Commander and Chief Controller was Squadron Leader J. A. Tester, with Flying Officer Chandler as Adjutant. We were defended on our perimeter by a unit of the Beds and Herts Regiment, commanded by a very affable Major whose name escapes me. My improvised storehouse was the former squash court, under the watchful eye of my Service Equipment Assistant, Flight Sergeant Ekins, assisted by Corporal Cayley and three A.C.2 Equipment Assistants."

The group under Mr H. Larnder which had gone to Stanmore carried out important operational research work in co-operation with Fighter Command Headquarters. Known as the Stanmore Research Station, this group consisted of a mixture of established scientists and junior men who at this stage were devoid of either academic qualifications or recognition, in spite of which they achieved outstanding success in the operational development of the new science. While some of the scientists worked on extending the range of detection, Dr E. G. Williams carried out an analysis of the effectiveness of the existing early warning stations. A number of shortcomings were brought to light, not all of them resulting from defects in the electronic equipment but rather as a result of the geographical locations of the stations concerned. So efficient did this unit prove to be that additional research projects covering land, sea and air applications of radio location to gun sighting and searchlight aids were undertaken.

The New Year of 1940 came in bitterly cold, with severe wintry conditions. Even the edge of the sea froze. As a result of the wintry conditions there was little evidence of enemy action, though the Luftwaffe did fly nuisance patrols and did carry out attacks on lightvessels, Trinity House tenders and fishing boats. To counter such activities the R.A.F. flew defensive sorties, nicknamed Kipper Patrols, and the aircraft involved in all these opposing operations were tracked by the East Coast stations.

The hard winter also delayed Hitler's plans for hurrying the conflict to a swift conclusion. Initial offensive action on the northern flank of the line running across Holland, Belgium and Luxembourg with the object of defeating the French army and driving the Allies from the Continent was to have taken place as early as 12th November, 1939, but the beginning of the offensive, code-named "Operation Yellow", was put off several times because of the weather. The final blow for the Germans came during January when a Luftwaffe bomber carrying secret papers concerning "Operation Yellow" made an accidental landing in Belgium, with the result that the German plans were revealed to the Allies. Had the operation materialised the Bawdsey detection system would certainly have been fully stretched in giving adequate warning of the approaching enemy.

When the German offensive did come, bringing the "Phoney War" to an end, the British Expeditionary Force was almost miraculously extricated from Dunkirk. It was at this time that a Blenheim Mk. IV was equipped with an upgraded Air Interception set. Eventually the Bawdsey Flight at Martlesham Heath became semi-operational, but limited use was made of it because of the risk of losing the very few AI sets which were becoming available. On one night sortie over the North Sea a Blenheim Mk. I stalked a Heinkel He.111 bomber and shot it down; one of the gunners in the stricken bomber managed to fire back and his bullets started an engine fire which forced the Blenheim to beat a hasty retreat from the scene. It managed to return to its base, crash landing at Martlesham Heath. The Blenheim's pilot was later decorated for his bravery in saving the lives of his air gunner and AI operator, who were both trapped in the blazing aircraft.

Aircraft based at Martlesham Heath were among the first to make such sorties against night-flying bombers during the period following the Dunkirk evacuation. The sets they carried were of limited range, and it was necessary for the stalking aircraft to be directed by ground control to within three miles of its target before the AI operator could take over and use his set to home in on the enemy.

Having returned to Bawdsey after a time elsewhere, Dr E. G. Barnes and a team of dedicated scientists continued their efforts to develop the AI set, which was perfected in time for it to play an important role in the night battles of the autumn and winter of 1940/41.

This was a period of trepidation, and there were very real fears that the Germans would invade Britain now that they had occupied the Netherlands and Denmark as well as having taken northern France. On 31st May, 1940, orders were issued for all signposts to be removed, all milestones to be lifted and all village signs and railway station and signal box nameboards to be taken down. The idea behind such measures was clearly to avoid giving an invader any clue to his whereabouts, but when the Germans learnt of this particular move their English-speaking broadcaster William Joyce, known to listeners in Britain as "Lord Haw-Haw" and executed for treason after the war, announced that the British Government had ordered such a move to make the population "stay put" when the invasion came.

The dangers facing the R.A.F. station at Bawdsey were not lost on Wing Commander Turnbull, who as a Flight Lieutenant was appointed Station Commander there on the departure of Squadron Leader Kidd on 12th June, 1940. Squadron Leader Kidd had taken over when Squadron Leader Tester had been posted to Fighter Command some two months earlier.

"All sorts of emergencies presented themselves, especially during the Battle of Britain and the build-up to it," Wing Commander Turnbull remembers. "There were five officers and around fifty other ranks, occupying a prime invasion area — half a mile of cliffs was the only high ground — with an arsenal of five revolvers and about fifteen rifles, hardly any ammunition, and with the scattered Beds and Herts men to the north and south of us.

"A desperate call on the 'scrambler' to Headquarters, Fighter Command, brought immediate response. At nine the very next morning Brigadier-General Majendi entered my room escorted by two Staff officers and greeted me with the words, 'Well now, Turnbull, what are you belly-aching about?' A thorough inspection of Bawdsey's low cliffs and river banks followed, and our position was quickly assessed.

"Within twenty-four hours contractors were in and Bawdsey's expansive lawns were scarred with a deep trench through the middle and an extensive barricade of poles and barbed wire was erected to repel parachutists. Guns were placed at strategic cliff-top positions and a fairly powerful naval gun sited to cover the Point on the Deben estuary. In less than a week we felt a little more secure."

Britain seemed to stand alone, but not all had gone badly in the first months of the war. An early victory was the defeat of the pocket battleship *Admiral Graf Spee*, which was scuttled outside Montevideo to avoid a further confrontation with the Royal Navy, and following her sinking Mr L. H. Bainbridge-Bell, one of the original Bawdsey "boffins", was sent by the Admiralty to inspect the wreck. In particular he was to investigate the radio location type aerials with which the *Admiral Graf Spee* was reported to have been fitted.

As far back as 1937 Watson Watt had expressed the opinion that women would make better radio location operators than men, and by 1940 members of the Women's Auxiliary Air Force were being trained for this work. Wing Commander Turnbull remembers:

"During May, 1940, the first contingent of about thirty W.A.A.F.s arrived under Assistant Section Officer Lethbridge. During their comparatively short stay they were inspected by the much-bemedalled Squadron Officer Baroness de Serdaes, who had had a very distinguished Service career during the 1914-18 War. Kitting the W.A.A.F.s was a

The delightful formal garden with its long lily pond and neat topiary. One of the receiver towers can be seen in the background of this wartime view.   *Mrs Gwen Reading*

unique and amusing operation. It was too early for battle-dress and no tunic jacket was large enough for a rather buxom W.A.A.F. cook. This unfortunate young lady could only venture out of Felixstowe in those hot summer days wearing a raincoat.

"The girls slept in the Manor itself, in the small attic bedrooms, many of which were rat-infested. Our Scottish Medical Officer, Flight Lieutenant Ingham, capably and diplomatically dealt with one W.A.A.F. who was actually bitten on the face by one of the vermin.

"Several peculiar occurrences were reported during those early wartime days, such as when an aerial-rotating motor ran amok and instead of turning sedately it motored round rapidly, causing the tower to which it was attached to shake violently. Unfortunately the power switch could not be readily located and until the wayward motor could be 'killed' many apprehensive glances were directed towards the swaying tower.

"While on the subject of towers, it is reported that when a mechanic or aerial rigger became seized with fright or some such malady while up aloft, one of the W.A.A.F.s who apparently specialised in the task climbed the tower and gently persuaded the petrified airman down to the safety of the ground."

The girls' stay at Bawdsey was, as Wing Commander Turnbull says, a comparatively short one, but they were to return later in the war. Indeed, Bawdsey was destined to lose its separate identity as an R.A.F. station for a time.

"With the threat of invasion hotting up, Luftwaffe strafing raiders made their appearance and Mr Churchill"—who had by that time been recalled from the political wilderness to become Prime Minister—"decreed that it was expedient for the W.A.A.F. personnel to leave this exposed and vital station. This they did, going to Malvern some time later in June or early in July.

"One day stands out for me: an afternoon visit by the Duke of Gloucester, after which during the evening the Airmen's Canteen caught fire. Luckily the conflagration was quickly discovered and effectively extinguished—a Court of Inquiry was not required. On my departure in November, 1940, Bawdsey ceased to exist as a self-accounting unit. Flying Officer Earl, formerly a Warrant Officer, took over from me, becoming the C.O. of the Care and Maintenance Unit, with Martlesham Heath as the parent station."

That visit by the Duke of Gloucester was not the only one made by a member of the Royal Family to the Suffolk coast in the summer of 1940. No doubt the attention of King George VI was directed across the river towards the Manor and its towering aerials when he visited Felixstowe on 11th July,

1940, and inspected the defences at the mouth of the Deben, manned by units of the 55th Infantry Division.

Visitors such as those were welcome, but the Bawdsey operators were at that time engaged in tracking less welcome visitors such as the Luftwaffe float-planes which continued to carry out their minelaying activities off the Suffolk coast. On the night of 22nd April, 1940, four such aircraft were seen flying low over the sea between Bawdsey and Walton-on-the-Naze and apparently alighting on the surface only a mile or two offshore, perhaps to release their mines. Bawdsey and other East Coast stations also tracked the bombers which made scattered raids on East Anglian towns and the London area, the task being taken up by the Observer Corps once the raiders had passed inland.

Eight enemy bombers, probably of KG4, crossed the coast near Bawdsey on the night of 18th June and on the following night another aircraft, flying on an easterly course, dropped parachute flares over the mouth of the Deben. Perhaps it was on a reconnaissance mission, for on 3rd July the Luftwaffe made a daylight call, dropping high explosive bombs at Bawdsey without inflicting either damage or casualties, and following that up during the early hours of 18th July by dropping another salvo on Bawdsey, fortunately with the same result. Two nights later a German aircraft flew low over the area and, after circling anti-aircraft batteries at Trimley and Harwich which had fired at it, dived down a searchlight beam firing its forward guns to extinguish the searchlight before flying off.

Bawdsey was machine-gunned on 7th August, but only minor damage was caused and no casualties resulted. In the following weeks the Manor was twice the target of air raids but on both occasions it escaped damage, on the second occasion three bombs dropping harmlessly in the sea.

Realising the importance of radio location to Britain's defences, the Commander-in-Chief of Fighter Command, Air Marshal Sir Hugh Dowding, ordered that all radio location stations and sites should be specially protected at all costs. It was an order which proved difficult to implement in view of the R.A.F.'s overwhelming commitments.

The destruction of the coastal radio location stations was listed as high priority in the Luftwaffe's general instructions for the first phase of "Operation Sealion", the invasion of the British Isles. The radio location stations, known to the Germans as "De Te Stations"—standing for Decimeter Telegraphy— were still something of a mystery to them, though it was apparent to those who planned "Sealion" that the tall towers at those stations were connected with some device that was proving a thorn in their side.

The plan, received by the Luftwaffe on 2nd August, was to be put into effect on 10th August, 1940, which was code-named "Adlertag"—"Eagle Day". In the event weather conditions caused a postponement of the campaign aimed at the destruction of the Royal Air Force until Tuesday, 13th August.

Two days after "Adlertag" the Luftwaffe sent 1,270 fighters and 520 bombers, 1,790 aircraft in all, against the British Isles, making it an eventful day for the operators at the Chain Home stations. At the end of the day the Luftwaffe had lost 76 aircraft, the R.A.F. 34. In the early afternoon of that Thursday some twenty Messerschmitt Me.110s carrying 250 kg bombs and escorted by a formation of Me.109s passed close by Bawdsey as they swept inland to attack Martlesham Heath, whose resident squadron, No. 17, was engaged over the Thames Estuary. Only three pilots, Flight Lieutenant Harper, Sergeant Griffiths and Pilot Officer Pittman, were available to deal with the raiders. Climbing as quickly as possible to 20,000 feet in their Hawker

A German copy of the British Ordnance Survey map showing the "Radio station" at Bawdsey Manor outlined. This target map is dated July, 1942.   *Elliott collection*

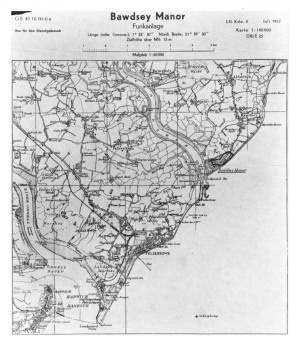

Hurricanes, the three pilots eventually got to grips with the retreating Messerschmitts and Flight Lieutenant Harper claimed one Me. 109 as destroyed. He was himself wounded in the leg and face and was forced to ditch his Hurricane off Bawdsey, being picked up by a rescue boat. No. 32 Squadron from Biggin Hill also raced into the fight, one of their number, Pilot Officer Grice, D.F.C., being shot down in flames off the coast; he managed to bale out and was picked up from the sea by a motor torpedo boat.

In those tense days there were tragic mistakes which cost the lives of R.A.F. aircrews. The Blenheims of No. 25 Squadron, commanded by Squadron Leader W. W. Loxton and then based at Martlesham Heath but on detachment at North Weald, were involved in one such incident on 1st September, 1940, while patrolling over Essex. They were attacked by Hurricanes of No. 46 Squadron whose pilots had mistaken them for Junkers Ju.88s. The aircraft of Pilot Officer Hogg was shot down with the loss of the crew, that of Pilot Officer Cassidy was badly damaged and forced to make a crash landing, while only that of their leader managed to evade the fighters and land safely at Martlesham Heath. The possibility of such tragic incidents was largely eliminated when all R.A.F. aircraft were fitted with Identification Friend or Foe sets.

As the threat of invasion grew, so tension mounted and on 7th September the Local Defence Volunteers were called out and troops put on standby as unconfirmed reports of imminent landings were received. Non-essential personnel were advised to leave the coastal area of Suffolk. At 20.07 that day the coded signal "Cromwell" was sent out to all Army units, putting them on full alert. But the invasion did not come, and the R.A.F. was not wiped out; the contribution of Bawdsey and the other Chain Home stations played a large part in helping "The Few" to win the Battle of Britain.

For the most part the operators at Bawdsey saw no more than the echoes from passing aircraft, but on 19th September the station was visited by a Hawker Hurricane I, V.6558 of No. 257 Squadron based at Martlesham Heath, which was forced to make a crash landing there after its engine had failed while on coastal convoy patrol off the Suffolk shore. The pilot, Flight Lieutenant P. M. Brothers, was not injured.

Conditions at Bawdsey in those tense times are recalled by Mr L. C. Johnson-Jones, of Hitchin, a Dubliner who had joined the R.A.F. as a result of an advertisement in an Irish newspaper which read: "Royal Air Force wants Radio Mechanics — Immediate promotion to Leading Aircraftman for suitable candidates who pass Trade Test." He had been employed in a Dublin radio shop as an assistant, battery charger and general dogsbody at the princely rate of a pound a week, and had studied radio servicing in the evenings.

When he was posted to Bawdsey it was the air of unreality about the area that struck him most forcibly. In Felixstowe everyone was in uniform and domestic and family life seemed non-existent, for all the boarding houses and cafes had become military billets; the place had the air of a Wild West film set where all the houses and shops were nothing but pasteboard facades. He soon learnt that Service life consisted of long periods of monotony interspersed with brief periods of intense excitement.

One of the latter occurred when the R.A.F. personnel were drawn up in a clearing in the trees surrounding the Manor for a pay parade. Mr Johnson-Jones glanced up at an aircraft flying overhead, and as he did so three tiny dots appeared beneath it. The dots grew larger until he could see that they were bombs; the parade rapidly grew smaller as the bombs whistled down.

Fortunately they caused neither damage nor casualties, but Mr Johnson-Jones still recalls his feeling that the German pilot must have rubbed his hands with glee at the sight of all those blue-grey uniforms in that woodland clearing.

Another air raid occurred one night while the airmen were in their billet in the Manor stables. Two nervous types who had donned their "tin hats" dived under the same bed from opposite sides; the clang as their heads met could be heard above the din outside.

A few days after his arrival at the Manor he and other airmen were walking along a path from the Station down to the beach when one of the party strayed off the beaten track on to the grass. Picking his lone way among several flat round objects, the stray airman fortuitously resisted the temptation to give one of the objects a good kick. He only realised how lucky he had been when a breathless and extremely frightened corporal appeared to tell them they were walking on the edge of a minefield of whose existence they had been unaware.

Sometimes there was excitement of another kind when inmates of a Borstal institution in the nearby village of Hollesley absconded. As the Station was encircled by barbed wire entanglements the only place where an intruder could enter was at the gates. To give warning of any such attempt the residents of the guardrooms strung a length of fishing line across the road, with one end tied to a suitable post and the other end attached to a broom stood up against the guardroom wall. On top of the broom was a dustbin lid, delicately balanced. Any movement of the stretched line brought the dustbin lid to earth with a loud clatter and resulted in immediate action on the part of the guardroom occupants, Mr Johnson-Jones recalls.

More frightening than exciting was the experience of Mr Edward Lipscombe, of Gravesend, who was on duty in the West Gate guardroom one day when Bawdsey was raided by a number of Focke-Wulf Fw.190 fighter-bombers. He and the portly boatman, "Tubby" Marjoram, lay on the floor trying to take what shelter they could when they were even more startled by the shrill ringing of the telephone bell. Mr Lipscombe answered, to be informed that an air raid was imminent and that "Air Raid Red" was about to be sounded. By that time the last Fw.190 was leaving the scene!

Luck could mean the difference between life and death on such occasions. Squadron Leader Arthur Williams, who served at Bawdsey under thirteen commanding officers and must surely have achieved a Bawdsey long service record, recalls an occasion when fortune certainly smiled on the Bawdsey airmen:

"The watches were divided into three, and on 6th May, 1941, two of the watches were off duty and enjoying a dance at the Cavendish Hotel, Felixstowe, while the third watch was, of course, on duty. Delaying their departure from the Operations Block due to the late arrival back at the

Manor from the dance of the relieving watch, it was the duty watch's good fortune that they were still 'at work'. An enemy bomber scored a direct hit on the Domestic Site where they would have been had they been off duty. Fortunately the area was sparsely populated at the time and only three airmen were killed.

"In these early days the transmitter and receiver sets were in separate wooden huts and some difficulty was encountered in tuning the receiver on to the signal. Necessity being the mother of invention, a concrete base was prepared and the wooden hut mounted on a crude turntable so that the whole caboose could be turned and tuned on to the signal, set at that time at 209° (Walton Tower). The trees at the rear of the hut were covered with wire netting in order to provide a permanent known 'blip'.

"At times it was necessary for the aerial riggers, and if they were not available, the operators, to climb the 360-foot towers to attend to the aerials, often during the hours of darkness. At this time the Station was guarded by a detachment of very zealous Scots soldiers whose orders were to shoot at any light visible during the hours of blackout. Shinning up a 360-foot tower in total darkness would have been somewhat foolhardy

Vertical photograph of the Bawdsey area taken by a Luftwaffe reconnaissance aircraft and issued in July, 1942.   *Elliott collection*

without a torch, and as a consequence these nocturnal expeditions upwards and downwards were often accompanied by the metallic clang of bullet on metal!

"Much of the equipment was of the Heath Robinson variety, produced on a sealing wax and string budget, but nevertheless the majority of it worked, and effectively at that!"

The enemy was very active in the area in that May of 1941, but he did not always have his own way. On 12th May a Junkers Ju.88A-5 bearing the code V4 + DM from 4/KG1 bombed Martlesham Heath during the early hours of the morning but ran into accurate anti-aircraft fire from local gun sites, crashing into the sea off Shingle Street, just a few miles north of Bawdsey. The following Monday, 19th May, a low-flying Junkers Ju.88 was hit by machine-gun fire from the paddle minesweeper *Princess Elizabeth* and crashed into the sea off the mouth of the Deben.

The existence of Bawdsey was certainly well known to the Germans, as is clear from the air photographs and maps captured by Allied forces at the end of the war. What seems to have been a determined attempt to put an end to the R.A.F. activities at the Manor was made at midnight on 14th January, 1942, when a parachute mine was dropped at Bawdsey. Fortunately it exploded outside the R.A.F. site and the only result was a large hole in a pasture and damage to a cattle shed. Another night raid occurred on 9th August, 1942, when both high explosive and incendiary bombs rained down on the Station perimeter at East Lane, but damage was confined to a house, which was damaged, and to a number of farm buildings, which were destroyed.

All these raiders and many others were tracked by the radar operators at Bawdsey, but this was by no means the full extent of their work for they also tracked Allied aircraft setting off for and returning from air raids on Germany and Occupied Europe. The Station's ability to track such aircraft was used to particularly good effect on 6th December, 1942, when a Lockheed Ventura II medium bomber serialled AE.697 and coded "P" of No. 21 Squadron based at Methwold in Norfolk ditched in the sea seven miles off Bawdsey as it returned from the ill-fated daylight raid, code-named "Operation Oyster", on the Phillips electrical factory at Eindhoven in Holland. The crew was able to escape from the bomber before it sank and was picked up by an Air Sea Rescue launch from Felixstowe directed to the scene by Bawdsey's plotters.

Sometimes the raiders that appeared over Bawdsey were there by error rather than by design. On 14th May, 1943, a Dornier Do.217K twin-engined bomber of No. 6 Staffel, II Gruppe, KG2, lettered U5 + CP left its base in the Netherlands with several other similar aircraft to mount an attack on the Chelmsford area, but in the darkness its crew mistook Ipswich for their target and dropped several bombs in the vicinity of the Suffolk town before turning for home. Leutnant Richard Ludwig and his crew of three were doubtless looking forward to their landing back in Holland, but when over Bawdsey at a height of some 8,000 feet the machine received a direct hit from an anti-aircraft shell. The bomber dived vertically into a sugar beet field known as Bullock Meadow at Red House Farm, Bawdsey, close to the village school, all four members of the crew being killed in the crash.

This aircraft was the first of its subtype to be brought down in Britain, but there was little of it left for the technical officers to study. The greater part of the wreckage was buried in a very large crater. The unit to which it belonged lost another aircraft only five minutes later when a De Havilland Mosquito night fighter sent it down in flames off Orfordness, and a third was later shot down further out at sea.

A funeral service was conducted for the crew of the Dornier which crashed at Bawdsey, and Mr Lipscombe remembers the occasion:

> "The local verger was also the Station coalman, and on the day of the service he arrived at the church wearing a cassock as his official vestment. But as this was rather on the short side, it allowed a large pair of coaldust-begrimed boots to be seen, while further up his legs lengths of string could be seen holding up his trouser bottoms."

During October, 1980, an excavation party from the Norfolk and Suffolk Aviation Museum at Flixton, Suffolk, recovered a great deal of the wreckage of this aircraft, and the author has a cylinder, complete with valves and valve springs, from one of the two BMW radial engines.

At this stage of the war the Luftwaffe's night bombers were being increasingly replaced by fast low-flying fighter-bombers which carried out hit-and-run raids on places like Bawdsey, Orfordness and Aldeburgh. The day after the crash of the Dornier at Bawdsey the area was strafed by several Focke-Wulf Fw.190s of Staffel 10, two houses in the village being damaged. One of the raiders crashed into the sea near the Cork lightvessel, the body of its pilot later being picked up from the water. Similar aircraft came again on 2nd June at a quarter past five in the morning when, after having dropped a few bombs and strafed the villages of Bawdsey, Alderton and Shottisham, they attacked the dock area of Ipswich. As they approached their target one of the Fw.190s, flying lower than its companions, clipped the trees in Holywells Park and then, losing altitude, struck one of the dockside cranes and plunged into Ipswich Dock, killing its young pilot.

By this time British night fighters were making good use of the AI radar developed at Bawdsey which made it possible for the fighter pilots to stalk and attack the enemy in complete darkness. During the night of 14th July, 1943, a German bomber was shot down into the sea five miles off Bawdsey by a De Havilland Mosquito. A popular deception put about at this time to explain the success of the night fighters using the still-secret AI radar was that the successful R.A.F. night fighter pilots such as Group Captain John Cunningham lived on a diet of raw carrots to improve their night vision.

This was the era of "Dig for Victory", a means of producing more home-grown vegetables so as to cut the need for imports and eke out food supplies. The Services participated in this campaign and Bawdsey ran away with the No. 60 (Signals) Group prize for the best-kept garden. Situated as they were, they must have had at least a head start on other gardeners within the Group, for Bawdsey with its wonderful gardens was well suited to food production and the gardens contributed in no small way to the provisioning of the Station.

Designed as a night fighter, the Bristol Beaufighter was equipped with A.I. radar, the aerials for this set being visible on the wing leading edges and on the nose.
British Aircraft Corporation

The training school established as far back as 1937 by Squadron Leader R. G. Hart was the forerunner of other training units which existed at Bawdsey alongside the operational radar station throughout the war and, indeed, throughout the life of the Station. Wartime memories of the Filter School are recalled by Mr Denys Hall, who was posted there as, to quote his own words, "a Corporal (Unpaid) Instructor" at the school, which was under the same Commanding Officer as the operational station:

"I instructed R.A.F. and W.A.A.F. personnel in the technical aspects of the interpretation of radio location information, not the electronic side of the equipment. This was a duty I had performed at the Radio School at Yatesbury in Wiltshire after passing out at the School. We also ran a course for senior aircrew, Wing Commanders and Squadron Leaders, to explain to them how the information was interpreted before being displayed on the Operations Room map table.

"Life at the School was very good, with regular dances at the Manor and also one or two pleasant hostelries on the other side of the river. We had several estate cottages which were very pleasant, two to a room, and it was a pretty walk through the woods to the cookhouse. The W.A.A.F. personnel lived in the Manor, as did the officers.

"I went to the Officers' Training School at Cosford and eventually returned to Bawdsey, via Northern Ireland, on a refresher couse. But my previous stay as a corporal had been far more enjoyable and worthwhile."

By 1943 the W.A.A.F.s had returned to Bawdsey and were playing an important part in the life of the station, both on the operational and the social sides. Mrs Gwen Reading, of Chandlers Ford, Hampshire, was "in residence" at the Manor during 1943 and remembers those times and the faces that were familiar to her then:

"In 1943 R.D.F. was still very secret — we dare not breathe a word about it or our work to anyone outside. Even the locals still speculated about 'death rays'. All the non-technical staff were selected for their integrity and the Commanding Officer, who came into the non-technical category, was not permitted to enter the technical area.

"I was a C.H. (Chain Home) operator, then L.A.C.W. Arnold. The C.H., C.H.L. and K sites were always very busy except during very poor weather conditions. Bawdsey was frequently complimented by R.A.F. Stanmore (Headquarters) on its general performance and accurate estimation of numbers of aircraft. I remember being 'on the tube' on the occasion when the largest number of aircraft ever seen by a station at one time was plotted. My estimation was I believe, 1,950, mainly friendly but some hostile and others unidentified — that was during 1944.

"We frequently plotted aircraft showing S.O.S. (broad I.F.F.) and sometimes we would be asked by Stanmore to concentrate on such an aircraft, leaving the nearby stations to cope with the remaining activity. Often these aircraft limped in at a painfully slow speed, getting lower and lower and sometimes finally disappearing while still over the sea. On other happier occasions we plotted the broad I.F.F. right in over the station, eventually sending someone outside our building to get a 'visual' as it chugged slowly overhead.

"In the days of large bomber forces going out over the East Coast we often plotted the Pathfinders, flying in advance of the main force, about a dozen single aircraft spaced about twenty miles apart, and these usually were Mosquitoes — the only aircraft type that we could identify. As the structure of this aircraft was mainly wood, it produced a distinctive heating echo, different from that of an all-metal airframe. The husband of one of the W.A.A.F. supervisors was a Mosquito pilot and we often wondered if he had just passed over our station. We found ourselves endeavouring to count them out and then count back in again — Falklands style.

"The old Rx Block proudly housed our two main receivers which were complete with electronic plot conversion, the very last word in equipment. We also had the 'Buried R' which contained a much earlier receiver and this seemed to pick up very little. When we did get echoes on the 'Buried R' equipment the grid reference had to be worked out manually. This receiver was our stand-by equipment if faults occurred on both main receivers, and in the event of this happening a member of the watch would be despatched to the 'Buried R' to get it operational again in advance of the main working party. This entailed a very eerie 300-400-yard walk through the dark woods. When I was called upon to perform this duty in the wee small hours my speed along this path was well up to record standards. I have no recollections of difficulties in getting the receiver operational, but we never did succeed in getting the telephone lines linked through correctly.

"Names I remember include Dorothy Rawle, whom I still see from time to time, Alice Murley, Peggy Butler, the Miley sisters, Denise and

W.A.A.F.s returning to duty after lunch.
Eastern Daily Press

Elaine, Corporal Jane Durrell from the Channel Islands, and an airman named Les Wilkins who was a wonderful dancer. Others were Les Smith, L.A.C. Bonnington, Ray Norton and Sergeant Jean Waters.

"On the social side I think that it was the ferry which made Bawdsey so different from any other station. Everything was synchronized to fit in with the ferry sailings. The timetable was very strictly adhered to and most of the W.A.A.F.s had bicycles parked at the Manor for quick transport to the ferry. In very rough weather the ferry could not operate, which meant that we were confined to camp unless we were prepared to hitch-hike to Woodbridge. Since our own transport seemed to be the only users of the Bawdsey-Woodbridge road we could not be sure of getting very far.

"There were of course the little privately-owned buses which operated between Felixstowe Ferry and Felixstowe Town. The driver's name was Albert and he talked incessantly in a strong Suffolk brogue. Before the journey was completed we were usually battling to conceal our giggles. I suppose that at the age of twenty most things seem amusing; certainly the fact that Albert said so much and that we did not comprehend a word invariably reduced us to a state of near collapse.

"I remember one occasion when Dorothy Rawle and I had spent the day in Ipswich but did very badly in our efforts to hitch a lift back to Felixstowe. Finally we had to take the last train from somewhere midway between Ipswich and Felixstowe, probably Orwell station, and then a taxi from Felixstowe station to the ferry. Alas after all this effort we arrived to see the last (11.30 p.m.) ferry boat halfway across the Deben. We knocked up one of the local fishermen and begged him to row us across. This he did at a price of two shillings plus a kiss firmly implanted on Dorothy's cheek. We finally reached the Guard Room at ten minutes past midnight, and I was on my first charge! Next day when we were marched before the

Beauty on the beach: off-duty "residents" pose for the photographer in 1944. Bawdsey must have been the only wartime R.A.F. station where personnel wore "civvies" within the camp confines.

Mrs Gwen Reading

W.A.A.F. C.O. we received only a reprimand. L.A.C.W. Nora Partington, who had been enlisted as escort, received a greater telling-off than we did because she giggled so much throughout the proceedings.

"I occupied two different rooms during my stay in the Manor, one in the White Tower, Room 50 and the other in the Red Tower, Room 18. The White Tower had been the servants' quarters and was pretty spartan, while the Red Tower contained beautifully fitted rooms and the 'Baron's Bathroom' — great luxury! We often slept on the roof after night watches during the summer days.

"A small stretch of the beach was cleared of mines and defences and opened up for our use, so we frequently bathed. I remember one or two illegal midnight bathing parties and how we always forgot that the sound of our shrieks carried in the still night air up to the Manor.

"The United States Army Air Force at Martlesham Heath sent transport to take any interested W.A.A.F.s to their dances at that station. The main attraction there was the quality and quantity of the refreshments provided. We were always enthusiastic about the ice-cream which they 'laid on', as production of this delight was banned in wartime Britain. We never did perfect a way to bring back supplies of this delectable commodity in an unmelted state to our friends at the Manor.

"Regular Sunday evening dances were held in the Manor ballroom and enthusiastic dancers, myself included, arrived early to have a few enjoyable rounds of the floor before the main crowd arrived. I often attended the Sunday evening service at the Methodist Church in Felixstowe, always leaving during the singing of the last hymn in order to catch the bus back to the ferry and to ensure getting back to the dance in good time. I expect that the good folk in the congregation thought that the poor little W.A.A.F. was always rushing back to go on urgent duty."

On the East Anglian installations, or East Coast stations as they were known, the transmitter towers were of steel construction, 360 feet high with the four corner feet splayed out at the base. A gentle taper brought the corner structural members to a parallel configuration as they reached upwards. The aerials, weighing some two and a half tons, were slung between the four towers. Hauled into their lofty positions by winches on the ground, the cables were kept taut by large concrete blocks which slid up and down on the ground in angle iron guide rails. The receiver towers were smaller at 240 feet and were constructed of pickled creosoted timber with metal ties. The aerials, copper tube dipoles in the form of crosses, were situated at three levels.

Transmitters were of the Metropolitan Vickers Type T.1940 with air-cooled valves and thyratrons converted from Type T.1583 which had two water-cooled valves supplied from a 400-gallon distilled water tank under the floor. Receivers in use were Cossor RF.8, with RF.7 and RF.6 in the older units. The RF.8 had an electrical range marker which the operator moved until it coincided with the echo or blip, then he flipped the D.F. out with the Gavis, pressed the control buttons and the height, range and bearing was worked out by means of a G.P.O. calculator, an early type of computer, which looked exactly like a telephone exchange. The resulting figures were shown on a screen in front of the plotting table.

Each station had two transmitters, individually housed in a brick building surrounded by an earth blast wall. The receivers were housed in similar buildings, usually sited about one-third to half a mile distant and connected by land line for the synchronisation of transmitter and receiver. This was essential as when the transmitter pulsed, the time base of the receiver was also triggered. Transmitters pulsed at 12½, 25 and 50 pulses per second, with peak power at about 1.8 megawatts, the anode voltage about 35 kV, the Screen Grid at 16 kV and the Control Grid at 2.5 kV. The transmitter had to be tuned for maximum power and near enough perfect balance of current on each pair of valves. The output stage was separate from the drive and modulator stages

71

and also housed the controller gear for all the cooling fans. Between the output and drive stages was a control desk where all the fans were controlled and power supplies switched. The high tension voltages could also be wound up or increased by means of a tapping switch on an auto-transformer which was also situated in the control cabinet.

Different types of radar station were to be found at places around the coast. One of these, originally a Chain Home Low unit, was on the low cliffs at Dunwich, on the Suffolk coast to the north of Bawdsey. This station, which came into operation in 1940, had its aerial on top of a 180-foot steel tower, the four concrete feet of which still remain today. Later the C.H.L. unit was superseded by a Type 16 radar remembered by Mr Reginald O'Neil, who believes that only four of this type were built, the others being the prototype at the R.R.E. at Malvern, and operational stations at Beachy Head and at Ventnor, Isle of Wight. Mr O'Neil went abroad with one of these, No. 16004 Air Ministry Experimental Station, when it was sent to Malta to cover the invasion of Sicily and then to Corsica for use in the assault on Southern France. He later returned to the Dunwich site.

The Type 16 was a 50-centimetre radar built into a 30-foot parabolic dish, the dipole being mounted on an arm that moved up and down eight times a second and so nicknamed "the Wobalater". The prime purpose of this unit was to control fighter sweeps and escorts for daylight bombing missions at extreme ranges. From Dunwich it was possible to exercise control of operations beyond Berlin, and sweeps into Southern France were controlled from the site at Calvi on the north-west coast of Corsica. At the time it came into use it was the most accurate and far-reaching radar available; the design is said to have been aided by the results of the Bruneval raid in which Commandos seized a German radar installation on the French coast.

With the entry of America into the war and the arrival in Britain of vast numbers of American soldiers and airmen it became highly necessary to promote co-operation between the Allies. During 1944 the Bawdsey Operations Book shows that this co-operation was proceeding well; during January five American officers who were on the operational staff of the Bawdsey Filter Room were posted to West Beckham, near Sheringham in Norfolk, to give them full operational experience at an out-station.

Bawdsey saw many of the crippled aircraft of the 8th United States Army Air Force struggling back home after their nightmare experiences over Occupied Europe by daylight. Smoking wrecks, often remaining airborne only with the greatest difficulty, they crept in over the North Sea as their pilots struggled to reach the sanctuary of the English coast. Not all were as fortunate as the B.17 Fortress which ditched off the Manor during the afternoon on 8th March, 1944.

During May and June of that year other B.17 Fortresses, the only examples of that American-built type to be used by the R.A.F., flew over the Bawdsey area as they plotted the polar diagram of the Station and the field strengths over enemy territory of both the Bawdsey and Dunwich stations. These black-painted aircraft belonged to the R.A.F.'s secret No. 100 Group which was concerned with radio countermeasures.

One of the simplest yet most masterful of all countermeasures was that code-named "Window" by the British, "Duppel" by the Germans and "Chaff" by the Americans. It was nothing more than bundles of metallic strips or metal-coated paper strips which, falling from the sky, completely disrupted

Two sisters serving on the same station: Elaine and Denise Miley relax on the beach at Bawdsey in 1944.
Mrs Gwen Reading

the electronic detection gear employed by both sides. It had been conceived at the time of the early radio location experiments at Orfordness and Bawdsey, but work on this countermeasure was intensified early in 1942 when Wing Commander D. A. Jackson, O.B.E., D.F.C., A.F.C., D.Sc.(Oxon), F.R.S. took charge of the project.

It was decided that the metallic strips would be dropped through a chute in the aircraft's fuselage floor as a bundle which would break apart and scatter once clear of the bomber. The aluminium strips were each designed as micro-dipoles in proportion to the signal to be blotted. Such was the lightness of the material employed that it took some two hours for a strip dropped from 5,000 feet to reach the ground, while a standard six-ounce bundle which contained approximately 6,000 strips was found to give the same return signal to the Luftwaffe radar stations as three Lancaster bombers—a frightening sight to the men scanning the screens of the defence radar.

One of the great problems confronting the scientists, having established the effectiveness of this deception device, was when to launch it. Much depended on what would be the enemy's reactions, as after its use for the first time the enemy would be able to pick up the widely scattered thin metal strips and it would no longer be secret.

The Prime Minister, Mr Winston Churchill, sat in on a Defence Committee meeting on 22nd June, 1943, the object of the meeting being to determine a launching date for the device. One of the factors to be considered was retaliatory attacks by the Luftwaffe using "Duppel", but as attacks on the British isles had only been on a limited scale over the past twelve months it was considered safe to go ahead. Hermann Goering had also been apprehensive of its use for fear of reprisal.

"Window" was first used by the Royal Air Force during the course of an 800-plus-aircraft raid on the German city of Hamburg during the night of 24/25th July, 1943. The introduction of this deception device was a great success and showed up in the fact that casualties suffered by the R.A.F. bomber force were greatly reduced as the Luftwaffe night fighters could not be directed to their targets by the semi-inoperative ground control and airborne interception radar. Information gleaned after the struggle from German records stated that the Luftwaffe defence system was taken by surprise on the first "Window" operation.

When the Luftwaffe stepped up its attacks on the British Isles during and after October, 1943, the effectiveness of the anti-aircraft guns with their radar detector gear was impaired by the raiders dropping "Duppel". After October it would appear that every German aircraft dropped the radar-confusing strips, which could affect an area 50 miles long by 25 miles wide, and again the pre-war sound locators had to be called into service. Eventually countermeasures restored the effectiveness of the detector sets and the enemy night bomber losses mounted as a result.

The supplying of "Window" and "Chaff" created tremendous production problems in the early days and the vast majority of the United Kingdom's metal foil resources were diverted to its use. In the United States of America similar difficulties existed.

Countermeasures to combat the radar-image-destroying strips occupied a great many of Germany's "boffins", struggling to produce an antidote to enable the defence radar operators once again to see through the "clutter" on their screens. Eventually they produced a new radar set able to detect the R.A.F. bombers in spite of the "Window" deception.

One of the outstanding applications of "Window" as a deception weapon was during the early hours of D-Day, 6th June, 1944. The enemy had sensed that something big was planned but just where the landing would be made was anyone's guess. The obvious place would be along the French coast opposite

Kent, in the Pas-de-Calais. This site commended itself as being the shortest route across the Channel, an important factor in such an immense undertaking. As we now know the main assault was directed from Southern England towards the beaches of Normandy, but in order to tie up a fair proportion of the enemy's defending troops it was necessary to make the Germans believe the attack would be launched elsewhere.

Avro Lancaster bombers of No. 617 (B) Squadron, of Dambusters fame, operating with Bomber Command's select Pathfinder Force, took off from their Lincolnshire base and, flying by a devious route, arrived off Dover during the very early hours of that fateful day. Taking up precise positions, achieved by the expert navigators of this experienced squadron, the aircraft flew in an exacting formation along the Channel coast off Kent and Sussex. "Window" was dropped at specified intervals, positions and heights as the bombers moved back and forth, up and down, each flight track taking them a little closer to the French shore. This sideways movement was estimated to be the approximate passage speed of vessels engaged on an assault course towards the enemy beaches. This ruse resulted in some of the defence forces being moved towards the approaching "ghost" armada and away from the actual invasion fleet.

"Window" was, perhaps, the simplest of the electronic countermeasures dreamt up by Britain's scientists. Others included "Mandrel", carried in pairs of R.A.F. bombers, which made life difficult for the Luftwaffe's night fighter force which relied on ground signals for directions, and "Jostle", another jamming device aimed at the night fighter force.

Perhaps the operators at Bawdsey thought that German countermeasures of some kind were responsible for the unusual signals emanating from Continental stations during the last week of September, 1944. Although these signals, which in fact marked the beginning of the V2 rocket offensive from the Low Countries, had detrimental effects on some radar systems, the Chain Home network remained operational. The first of the V-weapons had arrived at Bawdsey on 21st September at 04.27 when an air-launched V1 flying bomb approached from the north-east and crashed on Bawdsey beach just below high water mark. It dug out a crater 33 feet wide, but parts of the pulse-jet motor were recovered.

The first of the V2 rockets to fall in the area made its silent approach at 18.30 hours on 9th October, when it exploded over the sea off Bawdsey, its double-boom being clearly audible to the operators at the Manor as the sonic boom backed up the sound of the explosion of the warhead. With the onset of the V2 offensive the East Coast stations went into action, keeping a constant watch for the rocket missiles, an operation code-named "Big Ben", as Mrs Gwen Reading remembers:

"The C.H. operators had additional equipment named, I believe, 'Oswald' to plot the tracks of the V2 rocket bombs. To this day I hesitate to mention this equipment, it was considered to be so very very secret. We were only permitted to gaze at the screen for fifteen minutes at a time. When we recognized a V2 trail we yelled 'Big Ben at Bawdsey' into the phone connected with Stanmore. A few minutes later we would be instructed to change the film which was running within the equipment and develop it. I recall burning a film that I was developing on one occasion; to speed the operation the film was wound round a frame and spun over an electric heater to dry, and I failed to latch the frame securely and it fell on to the heater. We never did give Londoners the four-minute warning of the V2 which was possible, but nevertheless no doubt our work did assist in locating the rocket's launching sites."

The last bombs dropped near the Station by aircraft fell on 23rd June, 1944, into the Deben, where their detonation caused neither casualties nor damage. In the early part of 1945 war was still clearly evident, with V1 "doodlebugs" still passing over the district, though some of these flying bombs never reached the shore, being destroyed by gunfire off the coast. The Roughs Tower gun platform off Felixstowe was responsible for several. The last V1 to approach these shores was destroyed by anti-aircraft gunfire near Orford at 12.43 hours on 29th March, 1945.

For almost the whole of the war radar was on the secret list, although by 1945 there must have been a good many people who knew of its existence. An announcement made in *The Aeroplane Spotter*, a weekly journal very popular with air enthusiasts as well as members of such organisations as the Royal Observer Corps and the Air Training Corps, on 19th April, 1945, gave the public a little insight into this wartime mystery. "Radar, as Radio Location was now known, itself was a contraction of the words Radio Detection and Ranging," it said, giving the briefest of details about various kinds of radar including B.T.O. or Bomb through Overcast, known in the U.S.A.A.F. as "Mickey" and in the R.A.F. as "Magic Eye".

The use of these electronic devices did not become common knowledge until June, 1945, when *The Times* commented on disclosures made in an American journal regarding G.C.I. (Ground Control of Interception) and A.I., both British inventions.

It was only after the war that the public learnt in any detail of the contribution radar had made to the Allied victory and of the many developments which had had their origin in those pre-war experiments at Orfordness and Bawdsey.

Bomber Command used radar for bombing raids, the first system code-named "Gee" comprising three ground transmitters approximately 100 miles apart and radiating a pattern of pulses towards the target. Equipment in the aircraft decoded the time difference and plotted the results on a radar map,

On Thursday, 16th August, 1945, the national daily newspapers published pictures of radar operators at work; it was the first time the public had been let into the secret. This newspaper picture features the Bawdsey Operations Room and shows L.A.C.W. Gwen Arnold (Mrs Reading) seated right.

enabling the navigator to plot his position accurately, often to within five miles when 400 miles from base. Unfortunately the Luftwaffe discovered a means of blanketing the "Gee" transmissions and by the end of 1942 it was out of service as a bombing aid, though it continued to be used until 1970 as a navigational system.

At the end of 1942 "Gee" was replaced by a new bombing aid, known as H2S, a wholly aircraft-contained system which could operate wherever the aircrew decided to go. In basic terms, a radar beam was transmitted at an angle from the underside of the bomber and the return signal, displayed on a cathode ray tube, gave a good visual radar map of the terrain beneath the aircraft. This device needed a highly skilled crew to exploit it to the full, so it was deemed expedient that it should be in the hands of the more experienced aircrews and the now-famous Pathfinder Force was formed under the command of Air Vice-Marshal D. C. T. "Pathfinder" Bennett. The task of this force was to pinpoint the target, illuminate it with special markers and thus enable the main force to bomb more accurately.

The endeavours of the Pathfinders were helped when another bombing aid, code-named "Oboe", came into service. Powerful transmitters were set up at Cromer on the Norfolk coast and at Dover in Kent to send out pulses which were received and retransmitted by the bombers. From the information received back at the ground stations it was possible to transmit directions to the aircraft and to give bomb-release times over the target. Giving an even greater degree of accuracy than earlier systems, it had the disadvantage that the range was limited, although the higher an aircraft flew, the greater was the range of "Oboe"; at 27,500 feet a range of about 265 miles was available.

After the invasion of Europe additional transmitters were set up on the Continent which increased the effective range over Germany, although it was possible to direct only one aircraft at a time from these stations. As a consequence this device was limited to the exclusive use of the Pathfinders, in particular by the fast, high-flying Mosquitoes which dashed in to mark the target and were out again almost before the enemy realised they had been visited.

And so after all the activity and the panic of wartime, peace came at last. The Manor still stood in the shadow of the tall steel and wood structures that had played such a significant part in the preservation of Britain. It was still to have a role to play in the uneasy peace that lay ahead.

Sports day at R.A.F. Bawdsey in 1945. The creeper-covered face of the Manor looks down on a scene of great activity.   *Mrs Gwen Reading*

CHAPTER SIX

Into Peace

ALTHOUGH the ending of hostilities resulted in an easing of the load, peace certainly did not mean an end to activities at the Manor. Bawdsey remained operational, with duties now on a limited watch basis, and the Station became the home of the Radio School at which radar mechanics and operators were trained.

With its modified and newly installed equipment the Station was in constant need of aircraft to carry out calibration tests, and although there was still a good source of R.A.F. aircraft available it was found expedient to engage a number of civil aircraft, whose pilots were glad to spread their wings again after the restrictions of wartime. Among the aircraft employed was an Auster of the West Suffolk Aero Club based at Ipswich Airport, Nacton, whose task was to fly up and down the coast on a predetermined course and at a predetermined height so that the radars at Bawdsey, Great Bromley and Darsham High Street could be calibrated. This type of aircraft served at Ipswich Airport for a number of years, and one such aircraft made the last take-off from nearby Martlesham Heath on the occasion of its closure on 25th March, 1979; the author was on board.

After wartime neglect the Manor grounds began to look trim again, several airmen and airwomen giving up their spare time to assist in the work of restoring them to their former appearance. While the gardens had been tended throughout the war years the grounds had not been looked after; even in the post-war years the wartime defence guns remained intact in their emplacements to hamper grass-cutting activities. The artificial river which ran through the grounds, always affectionately known as the Jordan, was cleared of accumulated debris and the stone bridge carrying the entrance drive over it was repaired.

By this time every Serviceman had heard of radar, yet many of the men and women posted to Bawdsey still received quite a shock when arriving there for the first time. One Corporal arrived at Felixstowe Town Station, on the L.N.E.R. branch from Ipswich, having just been posted from a busy Fighter Command station and knowing nothing of the place to which he had been sent. Leaving the station he espied a W.A.A.F. and asked her the way to R.A.F. Bawdsey. He was somewhat stunned by the reply that you took the bus from the station to the ferry and then crossed by boat to the unit. "Bus and boat!" thought the Corporal, "what the devil have I come to?" In guarded terms he continued his interrogration of the W.A.A.F. "What do they have there?" The reply "C.H., C.H.L. and I.F.F." left him more confused than ever and forced him to ask outright, "Is it a fighter or a bomber drome, and what kind of planes do they have?" The reply "They don't have any—only radio location" frightened him more than a little.

For the first few weeks newcomers thought that they would never settle to the environment, but a change gradually came over them; after a while they grew to love the Station and hoped that the posting from Bawdsey would never arrive. Ex-residents all speak of their days at the Station in glowing terms. During the summer months all the delights of the holiday coast were there for the asking and off-duty hours could be spent indulging in swimming on the "Company Beach", sailing, walking the heaths, fishing and, of course, on trips over the Deben to Felixstowe and occasionally up the river to Woodbridge.

Bawdsey Beach with the steel Chain Home transmitter towers in the background and the reserve Chain Home receiver tower in the foreground. The groynes on the beach were built to stabilise the loose shingle. The short wooden tower in the centre of the picture carried the aerials for the buried reserve transmitter. *Mr Norman Bartlett*

Wing Commander Mummery recalls:

"My next connection with Bawdsey after 1938 was when I was posted there as Commanding Officer during 1948. At that time Bawdsey had three distinct types of radar equipment, C.H., C.H.L. and C.H.E.L., and it was as always a very happy Station. The W.A.A.F. girls lived in the Manor under the kindly eye of Section Officer Barbara Smith and the airmen in huts under the trees. The Sergeants' Mess occupied a Tudor-type block over the stable yard archway and the Airmen's Mess was in the converted stables.

"Bawdsey is singularly well situated. It had a private beach, acres of woodland and the River Deben running beside it. It had a sports ground on which I am told County cricket had been played in the days of the Quilters, and also a tidal swimming pool. To exploit these advantages so that they could be enjoyed by the mixed community of young men and women there the Camp Committee endeavoured to give encouragement to various group activities. Thus we bought a second-hand sailing boat and entered the weekly Felixstowe Ferry Sailing Club race, in which we consistently finished last but undismayed.

"We made a long spare hut into a theatre, complete with red velvet drapes, and put on quite ambitious plays. Grass tennis courts were laid and the walled vegetable garden rehabilitated. Needless to say, money was necessary for all these spare-time projects, much more than the P.S.I. could provide, so we went in for pig-keeping and that provided the financial wherewithal for the projects, as well as additional sports facilities and dining-hall appointments. R.A.F. Bawdsey was a Do-it-Yourself Station before D.I.Y. was the household word that it is today.

"My two-year spell at the Manor passed all too quickly. In peacetime it was by no means a typical R.A.F. Station. I dare say several romances flourished there, and there are no doubt quite a few middle aged people today, fortunate enough to have been posted there, who can look back nostalgically, as I do, on that charming place where history was made."

Mrs Sylvia Evans arrived at Bawdsey during February, 1949, and was initially billeted in a room above the Officers' Mess looking out to sea, and later in both the Red and White towers. She recalls:

"It's odd to remember that I did not enjoy Bawdsey for the first six weeks or so; there were several reasons. I was posted there alone from Yatesbury, Wiltshire, a place which I had grown to love. It was mid-winter and I came into a close-knit community where I knew no-one. I was put into a room in a gloomy part of the Manor with two other girls, neither of them tech staff. We were working night watches then, and I never really had much chance to get to know them. Everyone was a member of a group and I felt that I didn't really belong. I watched them from afar and also observed the shifting population of the Radio School. Then, suddenly, two old friends arrived from Yatesbury, failed radar operators, demoted to the fighter plotters course. They finished their courses and went in the end, but by then I had found my feet. The spring was coming, and best of all I was moved in with another radar operator. We had a lovely little room under the roof and overlooking the sea. There were seven of us tucked away in three rooms at the top of two flights of stairs and very much on our own.

"It was a unique way of living, working and playing together, and social distinctions were, generally speaking, forgotten. In our room above the Officers' Mess we could hear when they had parties and much of what happened. There was an officer there who had no ear for music and at a certain stage of the proceedings he was always put up on a chair and made to sing. It was only by the words that anyone knew what the song was! We had our own drying room on that landing. It was one of the corner turrets and had a door leading out on to the roof. One afternoon, following a hair-washing session, three of us climbed up the main ridge and sat on the highest point admiring the view. Two officers came along the terrace below and we were silent, hoping they wouldn't see us, but they did and solemnly took off their hats to us. We went on over the rooftops, two of us barefoot, the third, finding her shoes a nuisance on the tiles, took them off and threw them into a bedroom window. Afterwards when she went to collect them she feared that they were not in the room where she thought they were and had visions of having to ask one of the stuffier officers for them. Luckily the window turned out to be in another part of the W.A.A.F. quarters, so all was well.

"Boy friends were a source of unending interest. The fighter plotters course provided change and variety and teatime in the Airmen's Mess on the day of a new intake was the time when they came under scrutiny and were looked over. There came a time when the male radar operators were phased out, although we got some more later on. However, one was somehow overlooked and rather enjoyed his unique position. He was a Glasgow boy called Jock Aitken whose accent was so broad as to be quite incomprehensible when he spoke fast, as he often did. He got enormous amusement out of these teatime inspections of a new intake and teased everyone by marking down likely partners for them. It happened that two or three of the fighter plotters I went out with had moustaches and he never forgot this. Sometimes he would place himself behind a moustached airman, making sure I could see him, and stroke an imaginary 'tache'; or he would eye the queue waiting to get to the serving hatch and remark

Off-duty smiles as four members of the Bawdsey staff enjoy a spell of relaxation among the steelwork. *Mrs Sylvia Evans*

with a sign of mock relief, 'Aye and there's one with a tache for Sylvia!'

"There was, of course, never any lack of things to do. One of my passing fighter plotters introduced me to bird-watching. He was very good at identifying birds by their song, and he also took to beachcombing and used to look for pieces of agate, carnelian and amber at the water's edge, although in two and a half years I found only three pieces of amber. Apart from that we found all manner of interesting things washed up after storms, seaweed and sea creatures and once a dead porpoise. We often saw porpoises out at sea, leaping among the waves.

"Among our unusual postings to the Manor was a marine biologist, Johnny Cooke, who took to beachcombing with great enthusiasm. He dug about in the Red Crag and found shark's teeth and various other fossils. He arrived in one intake in the spring and simply attached himself to a group of us who had taken over the conservatory with official permission. Another friend was Frank Gaunt, a commercial artist, who was asked to paint a mural for the Airmen's Mess and was given the conservatory as a studio. It became a sort of haven for people wanting, as they say now, to do their own thing. Frank painted there, I wrote, people came and played musical instruments, Johnny Cooke arranged his fossils and folk in the Dramatic Society learned their words and rehearsed privately.

"Frank also played the violin and taught us a great deal about classical music. We now had a flourishing Music Circle. A fire would be lit in the Ballroom, armchairs moved in from the Airmen's Lounge and a large number of people would come to listen to records. We could bring

On parade in front of the Manor on 16th June, 1949, is No. 2 Flight of No. 5 Radio School. Berets are beginning to replace the airmen's forage caps. *Mrs M. Beck*

knitting as long as we didn't click the needles! Afterwards we discussed the music, and Frank, who had the scores to all the great violin concertos, taught us to follow them through. They still remind me of those gatherings!

"I got my place at Oxford from Bawdsey on coaching from Victor Watts, who was the Education Officer. As he was a lawyer and I read English it was something of an achievement for us both. I believe I was the first W.A.A.F. to be given early release to take up a University place."

Personnel from several other stations were posted into Bawdsey to experience operational conditions when Exercise "Foil" was held from 20th June to 4th July, 1949. Others who came to Bawdsey for training were members of No. 3619 Fighter Control Unit of the Royal Auxiliary Air Force based at Ipswich Airport. This unit, run on the lines of a Mobile Radar Unit, trained radar mechanics, fighter plotters, fighter controllers and motor transport drivers.

Bawdsey played an important role in those post-war years as a base for the training of the men and women who were to operate the increasingly effective forms of radar then coming into use. During 1950 the Fighter Plotters School was extended and the Radar Supervisors School established.

One of those who came to Bawdsey in that year was an officer who is now the Reverend Prebendary Clive Taylor, vicar of St. Barnabas, Temple Fortune, London. He recalls:

"I went to Bawdsey in 1950 to open up a small school for Radar Mechanics (C.H.) and ran it for three years. The balance of R.A.F. and W.A.A.F. was such that it became known as the Marriage Bureau, though there were many stations which could claim that title.

"Stories about the ferry were legion and often apocryphal, and then, of course, there were the stories about the White Lady who supposedly haunted the Manor on moonlit nights.

"On a couple of occasions we had groups of girls from Roedean School spending a fortnight or so at Bawdsey. The authorities were at great pains to ensure that they were closely chaperoned, but the lads felt it was they who needed protection!

"My memories of Bawdsey are happy ones—it was a happy place."

Mr Reginald O'Neil, of Walton-on-Naze, first made the acquaintance of Bawdsey when he was an instructor with No. 3700 Radar Reporting Unit based in Hallam Street, London, which at that time used Bawdsey for training purposes. He recalls that much of the wartime equipment was still in use, with a Chain Home supported by a Chain Home Low on the middle platform of the transmitter tower nearest to Felixstowe and a Chain Home Extra Low on the middle platform of the northernmost tower.

"The Ground Control Interception installation, known as the Happidrome, at Trimley Heath alongside the Ipswich-Felixstowe road also supported this site," he recalls. "Both sites were fully operational up to and including 1952, after which new equipment was commissioned."

Trimley Heath had been built during the war with high-power radar equipment which during the closing stages of the conflict was used largely for ground control of night fighters. The operations room and other facilities were underground, the plotting rooms at Trimley and Bawdsey being connected by land-line.

Late in the life of Trimley Heath a fire which started in a transformer in one of the consoles badly damaged the underground operations room there. Fires in such underground installations produce particular dangers to personnel, one of them being the danger of smoke which cannot easily escape from the tunnels, but on this occasion there were fortunately no casualties.

In the early 1950s a new underground installation, always known as "The Hole", was constructed at Bawdsey to the north of the Manor. The contractors for the construction of this subterranean radar station were Trollop and Coles Limited, the radar equipment being supplied by Marconi Limited.

When the new station at Bawdsey came into operation the wartime one at Trimley Heath closed down, although it still exists and the surface buildings there can be seen just to the north of the A45 trunk road. It has been suggested in recent years that they might become an emergency headquarters for the local authority in what everybody hopes is the unlikely event of a nuclear war.

Another associated site was the radio telephony transmitter installation at Nacton crossroads, just off the Ipswich-Felixstowe road, a unit which could be recognised by the "Parrot cage" type aerials mounted on lattice towers. The aerials were so named becuase of their distinctive shape and were made of bronze. The high value of the bronze was the cause of the aerials regularly disappearing from this unmanned site. Investigation of the site following a report that the station had gone off the air invariably resulted in the discovery that the aerials had been stolen.

Gaps in the trees at each end of the Manor sports field were necessary for the safe arrival and departure of an Auster light communications aircraft often used by visiting high-ranking officers. It also conveyed them between the Manor and Trimley Heath, where the landing strip reached right up to the A45 road. In order to make this end of the strip less hazardous, the G.P.O. removed their overhead telephone wires and posts and laid an underground line. Nevertheless one aircraft did come to grief at this end of the strip, fortunately without serious results. Another feature of the Trimley Heath site was the R.A.F guard dogs which, being kennelled near the main road, barked at all and sundry and reminded any intending intruders that they would certainly get a rough reception if entering the site in any but the approved manner.

Mr O'Neil recalls an amusing incident which could well have ended in tragedy:

"We were staying in the Sergeants' Mess and one wild Saturday evening in November, a party of mess members and Marconi engineers ventured forth over the Deben in pouring rain and a miniature hurricane to sample the delights of Felixstowe. After a short time on the mainland it was agreed that due to the weather we would be far better off in the bar at the Bawdsey Mess, so we decided to return there. Two of our company, however, thought they would rather go to the Mess at R.A.F. Felixstowe. One was a member of the R.A.F. Regiment and the other the N.A.A.F.I. manager, and they told us to expect them back on the last ferry over from Felixstowe Ferry.

"They did not return that night and we learned with some amusement the following lunchtime that they had been picked up from a small rowing boat ten miles out to sea off Walton-on-the-Naze by a passing German ship. Its master had remarked to the pilot that English anglers must be a mad bunch, fishing in such terrible weather. Looking through his glasses, the pilot replied that even English anglers did not go fishing in lounge suits! They were picked up and landed at Thameshaven when the ship berthed.

"It transpired that when returning to the Ferry they became stranded as they crossed the low-lying Felixstowe Ferry Golf Links, which had become flooded, and their car stopped and refused to start again. By the time they reached the landing stage at the Ferry Charlie Brinkley, the ferryman, had long gone to bed, and so they were within sight of home, but with the River Deben between them and a warm bed.

"They decided that they could row, so they borrowed a pram dinghy and set out to cross the swift-flowing waters. Both being topped up with Dutch courage, it was not long before the R.A.F. Regiment Sergeant

One way of reaching the beach was by means of a wooden ladder on the cliff face. The coarse grass was planted in an attempt to stabilise the loose sandy soil. *Mr Norman Bartlett*

The R.A.F. Bawdsey Rugby football team, 1949-50, poses on the sports field in front of the Manor, whose ornate style of architecture is evident in this view.   *Mrs Sylvia Evans*

discovered that the N.A.A.F.I. manager, although an ex-airborne type, could not row a boat, and they were rapidly swept out to sea where they gave themselves up for lost. It is rumoured that the N.A.A.F.I. man took the pledge and never touched another drop of drink!"

Mr John Langford, of Ipswich, arrived at Bawdsey during the Autumn of 1950 as a member of Radar Course No. CH 12, under the charge of Flight Sergeant Ramsey, with Corporal Baker in charge of the Transmitter (Tx) Course and Corporal Tripp in charge of the Receiver (Rx) Course. The C.H. Mechanics Course was under the complete control of the Station Technical Officer. Mr Langford recalls:

"The Mechanics School was situated alongside the transmitter compound at the C.H.L. end of the site. When the Bawdsey course was completed the whole class of about twenty passed out as Aircraftmen First Class

(A.C.1) and were entitled to wear the Radio Mechanics' 'Sparks Badge'. Some were then posted to R.A.F. Chigwell, Essex, behind Loughton Grammar School, while others went to No. 3 and No. 4 Ground Radar Servicing Squadrons (G.R.S.S.).

"While at Chigwell the newly fledged mechanics were sent to R.A.F. Weeton, in Lancashire, to be instructed in motor transport driving and it was there that I became a C.H. Mechanic/M.T. Driver. Incidentally, the trainees had to take a civilian driving test, as there had been a lot of words in the national newspapers about the proficiency of Service drivers!

"Back at Chigwell I became part of No. 4 Q.O. (Quarterly Overhaul) Party whose duties were to inspect, maintain and carry out modifications to transmitters and receivers as well as the aerials. Part of our equipment was a pair of field-glasses for inspecting the transmitter arrays as they hung suspended between the 360-foot steel towers. Not the least of the maintenance jobs was the inspection of the red aircraft warning lights which were set at three levels up the towers.

"In charge of the party was Flight Lieutenant Humphries, who did all his travelling on a Triumph Swallow motor-cycle combination, and the Senior N.C.O. was Flight Sergeant Nicholas, who had been at Singapore and had escaped by spending several days in a small boat before being picked up.

"Another member of the party was Dennis Rigby, who before coming into the R.A.F. had been a stressman at the Royal Aircraft Establishment, Farnborough, and was an A.M.I.Mech.E. — it seemed a waste of talent at the time! Another member, Roy Kay, had been with the G.P.O. and also being an ex Air Training Corps (A.T.C.) member he had a service number close to mine. Wherever we were, he was always in demand for telephone repair duties or when trouble was experienced with the land-line which was used to connect the Tx and Rx units. One of the uses of the land-line was to ensure that the Tx was locked to the Rx, i.e. the time base trace on the Rx had to start at exactly the same moment as the pulse left the Tx aerial.

"Many of the radar sites, like Bawdsey, were situated in remote positions and as our party was a small one we were a close-knit community, living sometimes in a domestic site and at other times in a village public house and even at seaside hotels. We usually all lived in the same hut, including the dog handlers, although the dog lived in its kennel outside. At Bawdsey we would have the little hut near the Tx compound gate and when we had the tea brewed, the Corporal Guard would bring himself and his dog up for a cuppa! The dog always stretched out near the Control Cabinet and waited for its saucer of hot tea and biscuits.

"When the stove was temperamental, especially during the early morning, water for shaving was heated by standing an enamel mug on an upturned electric iron, while the more venturesome experimented with electrodes suspended in cut-down food tins — a highly dangerous method, designed for the tired of living!

"One of my duties was to write the reports which logged all the adjustments made, modifications carried out, worn parts replaced and valves changed, and indeed anything at all that had been done to the equipment. Shortly after I joined the party, the wave change equipment, channel change in modern terms, had to be removed as each transmitter was to operate on only one frequency. All this work had to be written up, including part reference numbers, in typical Air Ministry style. This was of course in the usual triplicate, but as there was no carbon paper it was truly written in triplicate. One day I had just finished this task, it had been checked by the Flight Sergeant, who then put it in a sealed envelope, and the envelope was collected from the Tx Block by the Officer in Charge, who placed it in the sidecar of his motor-cycle combination while he proceeded to the Rx Block, leaving his transport. When he returned he discovered that the cows in the station compound had chewed the Rx Reports, so three days' work had to be done all over again."

The warm summer of 1950 was instrumental in producing a bumper crop of very succulent blackberries on the estate, and these were eagerly picked by the residents both as snacks and for processing by the Manor kitchens. Sports day on 31st May produced good entries in all athletic events, while a display of

The cast of "Tons of Money", staged in December, 1950, by the R.A.F. Bawdsey Dramatic Society.   *Mrs Sylvia Evans*

arts and crafts was held in the conservatory. During August, the Bawdsey Dramatic Society under its resident producer, James MacInnes, presented the farce *Rookery Nook* and this was well received by the many who attended its run. Later during the year, in December, fired by its previous success the same group put on another Aldwych farce, *Tons of Money*, this time produced by Tom Trolley.

During 1951 much of the work was still experimental and Mr Langford recalls:

"We were asked by one of the senior civilian staff to assist in the construction and deployment of a large vee-type aerial. Although the boffin knew in principle what he required, he wasn't really sure of how to set about its construction. Eventually the aerial was put together with the aid of chalk drawings on the floor of one of the workshops, much as you would lay out the ribs of a ship. Burning the midnight oil, the R.A.F. men finished the job and erected it, and having obtained a satisfactory reception with it, sent one of their members up to the Mess to get the scientist to come down and look at the results. This he did and nodded approval, but then gave the shattering news that there had been a last-minute change of mind and the newly constructed equipment was no longer required and could now be dismantled."

During 1952 Mr Langford worked on the G.C.I. equipment at Trimley Heath and travelled between Ipswich, the site and R.A.F. Felixstowe by Eastern Counties bus each day. This procedure was adopted in order to economise on petrol, the Bedford 15cwt truck intended for the task of transporting the men remaining in the M.T. hangar at Felixstowe.

As Mr Langford had been trained in aerial maintenance one of his tasks was the upkeep of the various types of aerials on the Station. One which caused considerable trouble was the large rotating array at Trimley Heath, due to strain as the array turned into and out of wind. Many visits were made to repair the almost constant damage, a task which necessitated perching on the framework with a blow-lamp and soldering iron in order to bridge the element gaps.

One day while engaged on this task Mr Langford thought that if he soldered a flexible copper strip to the aerial element and fixed the other end of the strip with a 2.B.A. bolt and nut this would avoid much of the vibration trouble. Accordingly he carried out his brainwave, and as a result of several subsequent visits he converted almost the whole of the massive aerial array. As this was an unauthorised modification he thought it best to inform his Technical Officer back at Chigwell base. The officer looked at the "modification" in an approving manner and passed the information on to higher authority. Word then came back that this was to be an official modification and the first aerial to be treated as top priority was to be that at Trimley Heath — which was just about done in any case!

Mr Langford remembers two incidents which illustrate the often risky and indeed dangerous nature of the work, dealing as it did with very high voltages, often in experimental installations. One rainy day, the Technical Officer of the Maintenance Party, Flight Lieutenant Humphries, arived at the Tx Block on his motor-cycle combination, rather wet from his ride. Some trouble had been experienced with part of the apparatus which was housed in a steel cabinet, and so the door was opened and the officer looked in at the gear. Suddenly there was a flash and the air was filled with the smell of scorched cloth as the startled officer withdrew smartly from the cabinet, wearing a now peakless cap, still smoking, accompanied by a full set of singed eyebrows. Stray voltage, always present in these installations, had earthed on the wet cap peak; although no-one was hurt, the effect was, to say the least, spectacular.

On another occasion, trouble was being experienced with a large oil-filled capacitor which was failing to give its correct high voltage. At the same time the interior of the room housing the gear was being redecorated by local building contractors and as the weekend was looming up it was decided that the troublesome piece of equipment should be switched off, earthed and left for the weekend, giving the new paintwork chance to dry. Returning on the following Monday morning, Mr Langford, being local, was first on the scene; the other members of the party had to come from Chigwell. Starting on the

On top of his job, a radar mechanic poses at the top of one of the 240-foot Chain Home receiver towers. The taller transmitter towers can be seen in the background. *Mr John Langford*

The Bedford radar
maintenance van used
by mobile repair and
maintenance crews, with
V.H.F. radio aerial on
its roof.
Mr John Langford

job, he discovered that the high tension lead had not been connected up and had fallen down inside the gear. Loosening off the necessary bolts and fixing screws, he awaited the arrival of the other members of the crew, who when they appeared assisted with the removal of the heavy component down to the floor of the room. He was now able to put his hand down into the oil-filled assembly to retrieve the high tension connection, but as soon as his fingers touched the oil he received a smart shock which threw his hand clear and the oil spurted up all over the newly painted ceiling and walls. Reconnecting the earth lead to clear the apparatus of its charge, they left it for a while, doubtless to have the inevitable cup of tea, and on returning tried again. To their amazement he received the same treatment, while the interior of the room took on a second coat of oil! Such were the uncertainties of working with experimental apparatus, often on a "touch it and find out" basis.

The stormy night of 31st January/1st February, 1953, has gone down in history as the night of the great East Coast Floods, when a tidal surge piled up by a north-westerly gale poured down the North Sea and inundated low-lying coastal land from Lincolnshire to the Thames Estuary. Near Bawdsey wind speeds of 48 m.p.h., Force 9, were recorded early in the evening, and at 8 p.m. a massive gust of 81 m.p.h. (hurricane force on the Beaufort scale) was recorded. Two naval vessels, H.M.S. *Cheerful* and H.M.S. *Cockatrice*, were forced to anchor near the Cork lightvessel off Bawdsey as their commanders considered it too dangerous to enter Harwich Harbour, and the British Railways night ferry sailing from Parkeston Quay for the Hook of Holland was cancelled.

The Bawdsey "charm school": officers and airwomen gather on the Manor steps in July, 1952.   *Miss Stacey*

Storm warnings were issued to the R.A.F. stations at Bawdsey and Felixstowe and to the nearby Air Ministry establishment at Orfordness, and an anxious watch was kept on the rising waters. By eighty-five minutes after midnight on that fateful Sunday morning, 1st February, the tide had reached eleven and a half feet above the predicted level, two feet higher than any previous tide, at Landguard Point, just south of Bawdsey.

Squadron Leader Arthur Williams, living at the Boatman's Cottage, answered a knock on his door to find a fellow officer who warned him that the river appeared unusually high. After discussing the situation he went back to bed, but the caller returned a little later to say that the water was over the marshes. It was obviously time to leave. Picking up everything that could be easily moved, they loaded all the goods and chattels into a car and drove it to higher ground in the middle of the Station before returning to the cottage and sandbagging the entrance against the rising waters. Fortunately their defences held, and although the tide reached the cottage it remained dry within.

Showing selfless devotion to duty, the Corporal in charge of the Guard Room is said to have listed in full in the Occurrence Book all the station property which floated out through the gate. As the situation worsened he maintained his vigil from the top of a stack of tables, from which he was eventually evacuated to a safer position. When the water receded the Occurrence Book was one of the few items left intact in the Guard Room.

Far worse was happening at Felixstowe, where the flood took the town in the rear, breaking down the river walls and sending a wall of water on to an estate of prefabs and a caravan site. At the final roll-call, thirty-nine civilians and Service personnel lost their lives at Felixstowe that night.

Immediately afterwards nobody knew that the next tide might not bring the water just as high, or even higher. As a precaution many of the radar personnel from the Manor were moved into Felixstowe and billeted at a large house, Kersey Towers, in Tomline Road. While they were there they travelled to work each day by the little 20-seater Bedford bus operated by a one-man business named Aldous and then by boat across the Deben. The radar maintenance party's 15cwt. Bedford truck was stabled at the back of

Pilot Officer Ellis leads the parade past the Commanding Officer on 16th June, 1949. The natural beauty of the surroundings is clearly evident. *Mrs M. Beck*

Felixstowe Police Station in High Road, but owing to the very restricted space available to the truck's driver parking was a difficult operation, always watched with great interest by the local police, who sometimes offered unwanted advice to the frustrated driver.

In the aftermath of the flood Bawdsey was visited by the Duke of Edinburgh, who not only inspected the damage but, clad in a set of grimy overalls, participated in a strenuous spell of filling sandbags and placing them in position to prevent any further intrusion by the waters. New works that were being carried out on the lower ground near the river were completely flooded and in the end had to be abandoned.

In total contrast was the notable social event of that year, the dance held at the Manor on 2nd June to celebrate the Coronation of Queen Elizabeth II. The dance was the culmination of a day of celebrations in which all ranks had a part, and was different from earlier social occasions in that many of the lady residents wore becoming dance dresses, a glamorous change from blue-grey uniforms.

Once the new installation at Bawdsey had come into use the old G.C.I. station at Trimley Heath was phased out, while at Bawdsey the Chain Home equipment was taken out of service, being put on to a care and maintenance basis, and the Chain Home Low aerial was removed from the right-hand tower. The transmitters of the Chain Home Low system were manufactured by Metropolitan Vickers and were always known as "Fishfriers", because of their apparent resemblance to the commercial fish-frying apparatus found in the ever-popular fish-and-chip shops. The motor gear used to rotate the C.H.L. aerials was made by the British Thompson Houston company to a Ward-Kenard design.

Early in 1954 with the implementation of the Fraser Plan of 1950 for the reorganisation of Britain's defences Bawdsey's role changed from Reporting Station to Ground Interception Station, and at the same time it became a Master Radar Station/Group Control Centre. With this change it became one of the main G.C.I. stations in the Metropolitan Sector, and it is recorded that it achieved an average of 5,000 interceptions a month in its new role. Bawdsey retained its Master Radar Station status until June, 1964, when it became a satellite station under the control of the Master Radar Station at Neatishead, in the Broads area of Norfolk.

The 1950s brought in a period of growth which ended the post-war austerity and depression. The guaranteed weekly wage of a skilled butcher's cutter was a mere £9 10s. (£9.50), but prices were also relatively low and a pre-war Standard 8 car fetched only £150 and a superior modern semi-detached home in a much sought after district of Ipswich could be bought for £2,500.

It even began to seem that the Cold War of the post-war years was coming

The Type 54 head of the Chain Home Extra Low radar, intended for observation of coastal shipping and low-flying aircraft, situated on the cliff top just outside the main camp. Note the lift running up the tower and the rotating dish aerial on the head of the tower.

Mr Norman Bartlett

to an end when, at a Moscow New Year reception, Mr Kruschev proposed a toast to "the wonderful American people" and other wartime allies. "We do all we can to eliminate the situation called the Cold War and to ensure world peace," he said, adding that he thought the year 1958 would bring a slackening of international tension.

Such signs of improving relations were welcome, but the watch continued at Bawdsey and the other radar stations as Soviet aircraft flying over the North Sea apparently probed Britain's air defences. Those who like Mr N. R. Bartlett were posted to Bawdsey just got on with their work, knowing they were helping to maintain a vital link in those defences. Mr Bartlett, who served at Bawdsey in the 1950s as a Radar Operator (Plan Position Indicator), recalls:

"Located on the cliff top was the Type 54 head of the C.H.L. radar intended for the observation of coastal shipping and low-flying aircraft. The site was just outside the Main Camp. The Guard Room concealed the entrance to the underground reporting and control centre where all the operational people, except those on C.H., worked. As well as the Type 54, there was the medium range Type 7 and the nodding Type 14 height finder. A little later the long-range F.P.S.3 was installed. This was American designed, Raytheon, whereas all the rest were Marconi.

"The major item, however, was not located at any of these places but about two miles away, out on the marshes alongside the River Deben. This was the Type 8 which required a large open site for maximum operational efficiency. I recall going on Fire Picket there. A technician and myself were driven down a single track in a Standard Vanguard pick-up truck with our cardboard box of rations for the night. It was a late summer evening and being in the back of the truck I could not see where we were going but only how far we had come from the sheltering woods of the Manor site.

"We stopped and I had my first close-up look at the Type 8 aerial. It was basically a wire-mesh-covered framework about thirty feet wide and twenty feet high, rotating at four revolutions a minute. It stood on a concrete base and was surrounded by a low parapet.

"The grass, and there was nothing else but grass as far as the eye could see from that low elevation, hushed and murmured in the breeze and there was a gentle hum from the motor rotating the aerial. We waited for it to pass by and then slipped over the parapet and down a hatch into the control room under the array. It was a concrete cellar, lined with steel cabinets and instrumentation. In the centre the copper waveguide passed from the generator beneath the cellar, through the ceiling and hence to the aerial. The technician warned that I should not touch it—I would not be electrocuted in the normal way, but would burn from the inside outwards. In those days I knew nothing of micro-wave cooking!

"The main billets for airmen and airwomen were in two parallel lines of huts which were positioned around the site following the contour of the hill. These new buildings housed many of the operators and fighter

Left: The N.A.A.F.I. complex as seen from the roof of the accommodation block.

Right: A bedspace in Hut 35, with bedding neatly folded and pin-ups on inside of locker door.

Far right: Hut 35, which contained two rooms at one end each sleeping four airmen, a corporal's room and a small sitting room complete with brick fireplace.

Mr Norman Bartlett

plotters who had moved in from Felixstowe Air Station. The huts comprised two rooms across the end of each building, each sleeping four persons, a junior N.C.O's room, and a small sitting room complete with brick fireplace. In some huts double bunks were fitted so that the total capacity was eighteen persons. There were also two baths, two handbasins and two W.C.s in each billet.

"Bawdsey Ferry Post Office was housed in the farm buildings which lay at the centre of the Manor estate. The main road through the Camp ran in front of the Post Office and a path led from that point through a gap in the cliffs down to the beach, and was therefore always known as 'The Gap'. The Accommodation Block and the Sergeants' Mess were the only two buildings in the Camp that were not single storey. Billets for the N.A.A.F.I. girls were in the vicinity, but never became such a centre of attraction as they did on some stations, probably due to the presence at Bawdsey of so many W.R.A.Fs who had the advantage over the N.A.A.F.I. girls of working all day with the men.

"Being in a somewhat isolated position the Station invited a certain degree of self-amusement and the autumn was the big season for these pranks, as then fireworks came into the shops and were available for these activities. It usually started off by bangers being dropped down drains, and this escalated to their being pushed under doors and up overflow pipes which emerged from bathrooms. I hardly need add this occurred while the victim was in the bath!

The farm buildings which formed the centre of the Bawdsey Manor estate. The Chain Home towers appear to look down on the buildings, which included the Bawdsey Ferry Post Office.

Mr Norman Bartlett

"Billets were fortified, but nevertheless the pranksters still got through and it became popular to place a fizzing banger inside a soft object. The ultimate was the dreaded 'Bread Pudding Bomb'. A generous portion of Airmen's Mess bread pudding would be misappropriated and a banger placed inside it. When this exploded in the opposition's billet, blobs of brown gooey 'pud' would be deposited over walls, ceilings, bedding and airmen."

The early history of the Station was recalled on 20th July, 1959, when the Duchess of Gloucester unveiled a plaque in the Officers' Mess commemorating the work carried out on the site by Sir Robert Watson-Watt, as he had become since leaving Bawdsey, and his team of scientists. The plaque carries the inscription:

In the year 1936 at Bawdsey Manor
Robert Watson Watt
and his team of scientists developed
the first air defence radar warning station.
The results achieved by these pioneers played
a vital part in the successful outcome of
the Battle of Britain in 1940.

After his Bawdsey days Sir Robert served as Director of Communications Development at the Air Ministry until 1940, and then as Scientific Adviser on Telecommunications to the Air Ministry until 1946. Always a champion of women for radar work, Sir Robert furthered his association with the W.A.A.F. when in 1966 he married former W.A.A.F. Director Air Chief Commandant Dame Katherine Trefusis Forbes, D.B.E., Ll.D.

The relatively even tenor of life at Bawdsey was disturbed on 9th June, 1961, not by a blip on the radar screen but by a report that an airman had seen an aircraft come down in the Ramsholt area. A telephone message to the U.S.A.F. at Bentwaters sparked off one of the biggest searches by Service and civilian personnel in the area for many years, but the report proved to be a false alarm; nothing was found.

One lady who served at the Manor during the sixties recalled that on the occasion of the Commanding Officer's billet inspection strenuous efforts were made during the previous evening to get things ship-shape and Bristol fashion. When all was prepared the "girls" retired to their beds, but before sleep had intervened to relieve their aching muscles one of them espied a spider of outstanding dimensions reposing on the beam above her bedspace.

Action was swift. A chair placed on the bed enabled one of the W.R.A.Fs to climb up and dislodge the visitor with the billet-broom, while another stood by, Service shoe in hand, ready to deal the death blow. Due to the out of balance forces imposed on the chair by the girating lady poised on it, it responded to the law of gravity and all came tumbling down. Arms outstretched, the descending airwoman grabbed at the electric light as she passed it and on return to earth found that she had collected the shade, lamp and flex from the ceiling.

During inspection the next day the Inspecting Officer gave her seal of approval to the billet, and then just as she was leaving the "residence" turned and espied the light fitting on the airwoman's locker. Inquiring as to how this object had arrived in its present position, she was informed that when cleaning the billet the previous evening, the ladies had even done the lamp shades and in the course of this procedure, it had come adrift. This pleased the "Boss

Lady", who praised the billet members for their enthusiastic approach to the exercise and promptly "bawled out" the remaining billets for not being so keen!

During February, 1966, a fire at the Master Radar Station at Neatishead resulted in the death of two Norfolk firemen and caused the temporary closure of the Station. Again Bawdsey took up the role of Master Radar Station which it had relinquished less than two years before.

In the 1960s Bawdsey also housed the School of Fighter Control, which had replaced the earlier Filter School, a Controllers School and a Fighter Plotters School, all of which provided refresher courses for personnel who had been temporarily away from such work as well as initial trade training. Facilities were made available for training men and women sent to Bawdsey by foreign governments as well as for members of the R.A.F. and W.R.A.F.

Personnel picked for training at the School of Fighter Control were chosen for their alertness and the ability to make the right decision at the right time, for they were to take part in what must be one of the greatest battles of wits to be fought in our technological age.

The initial course was of ten weeks' duration and the students who attended were divided into five groups. One group consisted of active fighter pilots and radar navigators who had temporarily finished flying duties and

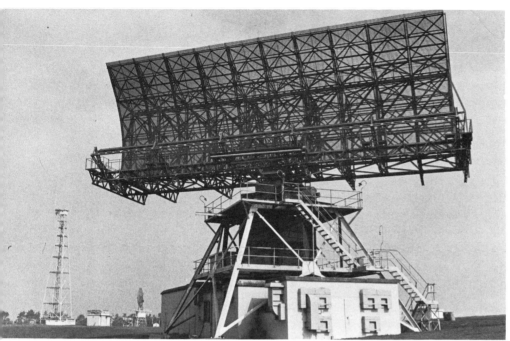

were transferring to the Fighter Control Branch. The second consisted of Officer Cadets who, having passed through their various courses, had decided on Fighter Control as their future job. Other groups consisted of Sergeant Controllers already in radar trades who came to be trained as Flight Sergeant Controllers and of N.C.O.s from other trades who were deemed suitable for training in radar and who, when they had successfully passed the Bawdsey course, went on to Officer Cadet Training Units for graduation as commissioned officers. The fifth group was made up of Commonwealth and foreign nationals who after their training at Bawdsey would return home to put their training into practice in their own Services.

The courses were fully comprehensive, with theoretical and practical work, the theory of fighter control and the use of the many modern aircraft as part of the training. Supplementary to the main course were the studies of ground and air communications, meteorology and navigation.

Housed in a brick building which was one of Watson Watt's laboratories in earlier days, the School of Fighter Control carried on the work of preparing for Britain's defence. In huts put up in more recent years, pupils were taught operations room procedures, using a large illuminated map similar to that found in operational ops rooms like that in "The Hole" at Bawdsey. One of the odd skills learnt was the ability to write backwards, essential for marking up information on the large transparent charts used in an operations room.

The School's chief instructor, Squadron Leader Fred Flowers, summed up the job as taught at Bawdsey:

"We find that this particular job of Fighter Controller is very much an aptitude. To do the job you've got to have the ability to make up your mind quickly, to decide what has to be done and then to do it without delay."

Not everybody has that ability. About 28 per cent of the trainees who passed through the school failed to make the grade; the other 72 per cent went on to serve with operational units, not just in Britain but in all parts of the world.

About 40 per cent of the courses was theoretical. The major part was practical, the students carrying out actual work under the watchful eyes of the instructors. Those who were accepted for training as intercept controllers were required not only to work out the course and speed to bring the fighter they were controlling into a position to intercept its quarry but also to make certain that the fighter pilot was not brought face to face with any other aircraft on the way.

Squadron Leader Flowers explained the attitude taken at the School:

"Flight safety is paramount, and this needs quick thinking, quick action. On a sub-sonic interception your aim is never to get within five miles of any other aircraft; if it's supersonic the range is ten miles."

Some students failed because of their inability to do two things at once. They could control the fighter and bring it into contact with the target, but they failed to observe another blip on the radar screen that indicated an airliner high on a scheduled route or a helicopter thumping its way out to a North Sea oil rig.

During this period the School had available the services of the English Electric Canberra bombers of No. 83 and No. 100 Squadrons stationed at West Raynham, Norfolk, while the high-altitude work was performed by English Electric Lightning fighters of No. 23 Squadron from Wattisham, Suffolk. In order to get the real feel of the job and so that students could see the other man's point of view, exchange visits were carried out between ground and air crews.

After the ten-week basic course students passed on to an operational unit training system, spending at least a further three months attaining the finer points of this most exacting task. The final achievement for each successful student was the award of a Certificate of Competence by the Air Defence Ground Environment Examining Board, without which no controller may operate.

The students regarded their calling as one of national importance and were proud of their vigilant watch on the skies and their part in the preservation of the airspace of the United Kingdom Air Defence Region.

The School of Fighter Control closed at Bawdsey after a ten-year spell in the home of radar and moved to West Drayton in Middlesex on 1st April, 1975.

With Bawdsey nearing the end of its life as an operational radar station, in March, 1974, representatives of a local newspaper were invited to inspect "The Hole", and following that visit Bob Malster wrote in the *Evening Star* on 21st March, 1974:

" 'It looks like an ordinary house, doesn't it?' said the Wing Commander as we walked up to what I took to be simply the guard room. What on earth did he mean by that, I asked myself. It was, quite obviously, just an ordinary little brick building like any of the other post-war buildings at R.A.F. Bawdsey.

"It was only when we stepped through the door that enlightenment began to dawn. We stopped outside a kind of wire cage, handed over our

One of the skills that had to be acquired by pupils at the School of Fighter Control was writing in reverse, a task needed to keep the large transparent information board in the operations room always up to date. *East Anglian Daily Times*

Press passes, and in return were given clip-on labels which we attached to our jackets, and were then ushered through a door in the floor-to-ceiling wire barrier. The door shut itself, the bolt banged home. It was like something from a science fiction film.

"I followed Group Captain David Rhodes, the station commander, down the stairs. 'We've got two floors down here,' he told me as we walked down a long corridor lit by fluorescent tubes on the ceiling. It was hard to realise that we were about thirty feet below ground level. The linoleum on the floor was well polished, the walls were painted a pleasant shade of deep yellow, and there wasn't the slightest trace of that musty smell one expects from underground installations. In fact, come to think of it, the air had that clean, fresh taste of spring."

Those representatives of the local Press who went on that tour of the underground complex were among the very few people, apart from the officers, airmen and airwomen who worked there, who have ever seen the operations room in which the staff peered down on to a huge map of the North Sea. For most of the twenty-five years of its active life this installation was hidden behind a blanket of strict security.

"The radar picture of the whole area controlled by the Bawdsey radar is projected on to this great map from below by a complicated automatic

apparatus which photographs a high-definition radar screen, develops and dries the film and moves the new picture into the projection gate every fifteen seconds.

"The master controller and his staff can sort out the blips which indicate aircraft from the clutter caused by freak weather conditions at a glance. And when news comes from one of the Continental radar stations of an 'X-ray' — an unidentified aircraft — on its way south down the North Sea they know just what action to take.

"The pointer indicating the aircraft is pushed across the illuminated map as it approaches the Bawdsey station's area. Soon the blip appears on the screen as it comes within radar range — about 250 miles from the Suffolk coast.

"In a dimly-lit cabin not far away the intercept controller peers into the radar screen, also watching the blip which indicates an aircraft. There are other blips indicating other aircraft, military aircraft here and there and civil airliners keeping to the airways which cross the North Sea. He knows what each of those is, but this mystery aircraft, this 'X-ray'?

"He judges its course as the blip moves across his screen, then uses the height-finding radar to discover how high it is flying. As it continues towards the British coast he brings a Lightning fighter from R.A.F. Wattisham to stand-by.

Opposite: Deep beneath the Suffolk countryside officers converse in a cable and pipe lined corridor which gives access to the underground operations room at Bawdsey.

Right: The radar map with its attendant plotter ready to move the marker symbols into position in the underground operations room.
East Anglian Daily Times

"When the fighter is ordered up to identify and shadow the unknown aircraft the intercept controller guides the fighter pilot on to his quarry, no more than a speck in the wastes of the North Sea but a precise blip on the radar screen.

"He speaks softly into the headset, giving course, height and speed to enable the fighter to meet the oncoming aircraft. As the two blips converge on the screen he tells the R.A.F. pilot that he will soon see the intruder, then gives him the order to turn on to the other's tail. Soon

Left: An English Electric Lightning F6 interceptor leaves a thin contrail from its wingtip as it speeds through the upper air.

British Aircraft Corporation

Opposite: A flight sergeant controller at his console in the underground complex at Bawdsey. Information on the wall board covers stations in Germany and Holland as well as British bases.

East Anglian Daily Times

comes the pilot's voice over the headset; it's a Russian Bear reconnaissance aircraft, doubtless probing our air defences.

"Thousands of feet above the grey waves the Russian tail gunner grins and gives the British pilot a friendly wave. Another successful interception has been arranged."

As in 1940, so in any future conflict the placing of R.A.F. fighters in the right place at the right time would play a significant part in winning the air war. But with new and improved types of radar coming into use, the Ministry of Defence decided to concentrate Britain's early warning system at three stations, Boulmer in Northumberland, Staxton Wold in Yorkshire, and Neatishead in Norfolk.

Towards the end of March, 1975, Flight Sergeant Brian Hunter lowered the R.A.F. Ensign at the Manor for what was thought then to be the last time.

A simple service was conducted by the Rev. George Vincent, Rector of Alderton with Ramsholt and Bawdsey, who had been chaplain to R.A.F. Bawdsey since 1956.

The Station was put on to a care and maintenance basis. During clearing up operations several early pieces of equipment used by Robert Watson Watt in the early days were discovered and removed for preservation as evidence of the pioneering work carried out on this site. Then in 1977 the remaining 200-foot steel radar tower, a local landmark for so long, was pulled down and

other smaller towers, concrete bunkers and defunct radar installations were demolished and cleared.

One of Bawdsey's longest-serving civilian staff was Mr Percy White, of Felixstowe, who had completed almost twenty-eight years' service when the Station closed. He was allowed to stay on until May, 1975, for his official retirement.

As one door closes, another one opens. The *East Anglian Daily Times*, Ipswich, for Friday, 5th December, 1975, carried the headline, "Bawdsey will be front-line defence missile base". This was followed by the news that a new No. 85 Squadron was to be formed on 18th December at R.A.F. West Raynham, Norfolk, and would be equipped with Bristol Ferranti Bloodhound ground-to-air missiles. This weapon in its Mark 2 form was a second generation missile, using continuous-wave radar principles and semi-active guidance to destroy attacking aircraft. This was part of the supplementary strengthening of the air defences of the United Kingdom announced by Mr Brynmor John, Under Secretary of State for the R.A.F., in a written Commons reply during December.

Bawdsey re-opened as an R.A.F. Station during the first week of August, 1979, equipped with Bloodhound Mk. 2 surface-to-air missiles, although speculation was rife that the twenty-year-old system would soon be replaced by a new type of rocket attack force. The much discussed U.S.A.F. Cruise Missile immediately came to mind as the Government announced a major "stopgap" programme of improvements to boost Britain's depleted air defences. It was believed that the new weapon would be based on East Anglian airfields and

British Aerospace (Bristol Ferranti) Bloodhound ground-to-air missiles.

might well be land-launched, although it would not be contained on fixed sites like the older intermediate range Douglas Thor Inter Continental Ballistic Missile (I.C.B.M.) stationed for a time in East Anglia but scrapped during the 1960s. As it turned out the Bloodhound continued in service and more detachments of this ageing but proven system have been set up in Suffolk, Norfolk and Lincolnshire as a first line of anti-aircraft defence.

On an indifferent summer's day, 27th June, 1981, a colourful group of people from all over the British Isles assembled at the Manor. Banter was much in evidence and hearty handshakes and back slaps were the order of the day. This was the annual Bawdsey Reunion, attended by many who had lived and worked at the Manor over the years. Wing Commander and Mrs Gilding, who had travelled down from Yorkshire, greeted the arrivals and many of the ex-Bawdsey people were pleased to recount some of their memories to the author. They also brought with them valuable photograph albums which were freely loaned to provide many of the illustrations for this book.

Stories that came to light, after an exceedingly good lunch provided by the Manor catering staff, included one concerning Air Vice-Marshall Pike's Annual Inspection when Wing Commander Gilding's young son ran across the Parade Ground to clutch his father's hand. To the young man's credit, he is now a serving officer in the R.A.F. Squadron Leader Hodges recalled that when he ran the Radar School he received new recruits fresh from Initial Training, so on the occasions of visits from high-ranking officers he was able to mount a very respectable Guard of Honour. Mr Joe Allan, of Bedworth, recounted how he was posted to Bawdsey as an Accounts Clerk, but as there was a vacancy on the Radar Course just starting he joined it and six weeks later passed out as a fully fledged Radar Operator. Among local representatives were ex-Sgt Coe of the Accounts Section, now an official of a local building society, and ex-Corporal Field, now head of the local police C.I.D.

A very special visitor was Mr Arnold Wilkins, O.B.E., the man who suggested to Watson Watt that they should try and purchase the Manor for their experimental work, who came with his wife. As he walked through the various rooms he had stories to relate of each and the ensuing stroll through the gardens among the old buildings was indeed a journey backwards in time.

Other members of the party sought out their old billets, the workshops, and even the site of the N.A.A.F.I. Strung out across the promontory were the brown rust-marked bases of the original towers, only one partly dismembered structure still standing, that of No. 2 transmitter. The spread of tree foliage has closed in the sky above the sites of the receiver towers whose bases now carry wooden frames where climbing plants flower in colourful profusion. Pushing aside a large elder tree, entrance was obtained to the dank dark interior of the once spotless "T" Block, now a large concrete shell, but so full of memories to the onlookers. As each old familiar door or nook and cranny came to light in the gloom the air was full of "I remember".

As one walked around the Station its vastness and spacious layout became evident. No other Station could be like it with its mix of glorious civilian buildings and the more austere Service ones. In great evidence were the flat red composition oblongs, once the well-polished floors of huts, workshops and the like; with their buildings now demolished, they face the elements alone.

During the spring of 1982 the future of Bawdsey Ferry became uncertain when as the result of problems involving the Ministry of Defence, Suffolk Coastal District Council and the 75-year-old ferryman, Mr Charlie Brinkley, the ferry stopped its daily runs across the Deben. The veteran boatman, who had taken the service over from his father, suspended sailings and put his boat into dry dock because he claimed that jetties on either side of the river were too dangerous to use. He warned, "If someone doesn't take the jetty over, as the Ministry of Defence is apparently no longer interested, then it might have to be dismantled. It could then disappear as a ferry."

Better news was received in October, 1982, however, when after prolonged discussions Suffolk County Council decided to take over maintenance of the jetties so that the ferry service could continue. Immediate repairs to the jetty on the Bawdsey side were costed out at £3,500, of which £2,000 was to came from the Heritage Coast budget. Suffolk Coastal District Council was to contribute £400 and the rest was to come from the planning budget and, possibly, from a grant from the Countryside Commission. The Property Services Agency had offered the jetty to the county council free of charge, with the proviso that if the county did not want it the jetty should be demolished.

Ferryman Charlie Brinkley had a double reason to celebrate in 1982, for on Boxing Day that year he and his wife Lilian celebrated their golden

Mr Charles Brinkley, long-serving ferryman at Felixstowe Ferry, and the *Late Times*, one of the boats used on this service which played so essential a part in the life of R.A.F. Bawdsey.   *T. N. Briggs*

wedding. Taking over the ferry from his father, who had operated the old chain ferries between 1895 and 1932, Charlie Brinkley became well known along the Suffolk coast both as ferryman and harbour master. Charlie and his wife received a special visit from the Mayor and Mayoress of Felixstowe, Mr and Mrs Tom Savage, to mark their anniversary.

With the rapid growth of the Port of Felixstowe there are times when there are more vessels arriving than berths, and it is not unusual to see several large vessels at anchor in the Bawdsey anchorage opposite the Manor. Their comings and goings are a constant source of interest to residents and visitors alike.

So, at the time of writing, R.A.F. Bawdsey continues to play a part in the air defence of Great Britain. To the Manor's occasional visitor, who perhaps knows nothing of its past, the plaque in the entrance to the Officers' Mess is the only indication of the tremendous work carried out there and of the enormous effect that work has had on the modern world.

CHAPTER SEVEN

Sutton Heath

JUST as Bawdsey made its most significant contribution to the winning of the Second World War without ever being a "normal" R.A.F. station in the sense of having aircraft fly from it, so the nearby airfield known as R.A.F. Sutton Heath was never intended as the normal type of operational station. It was not to be a station from which bombers and fighters would be despatched against the enemy and where anxiety would prevail until their return; no squadrons were to be based there, nor would there be any of the life-style familiar on ordinary operational stations.

As the round-the-clock bombing offensive against Germany and Occupied Europe built up, so the need for a refuge for crippled aircraft and their crews became more and more obvious. It had of necessity to be situated near the East Coast, on or at least near the main bomber routes, and as far as possible from any centres of population because of the danger of damaged aircraft crashing before they reached the runway.

The site chosen for this "diversion airfield", or "crash drome" as it was more commonly known, was the bleak, windswept heather-covered expanse of Sutton Heath, not far from where the famous Sutton Hoo burial ship had been excavated by archaeologists in 1939. Just off the Melton to Hollesley road, the airfield was situated in the middle of a wide stretch of coastal heath and Forestry Commission plantations. Not only was it as remote a spot as it was possible to find within the desired area of operation, but it enjoyed remarkable freedom from fog, a factor which was of the greatest importance.

Construction of the gigantic runway which would measure 3,000 yards long by 250 yards wide, 1,000 yards longer and five times wider than a normal runway, commenced during January, 1942. A 500-yard under-shoot at the East end and a 1,000 yard over-shoot at the Western end were also suitable for landing on if the need arose. Completed during November, 1943, its enormous surface covered some 159 acres. Situated as it was in the centre of a Forestry Commission plantation, more than a million young conifer trees had to be grubbed up in order to make room for the runway.

The emphasis was on this runway, with its eight dispersal loops along the South side, each capable of accommodating fifty aircraft. The lack of hangars and surrounding perimeter track and the small number of personnel initially posted to the station were also most unusual for such a large site.

113

Two other such sites were proceeded with, one at Manston in Kent and the other at Carnaby in Yorkshire, but Sutton Heath or R.A.F. Woodbridge was the first one to be completed. No other airfield could boast airfield lighting such as was installed here, as the Exterior Marker Lights were a combination of sodium and incandescent lights. There were no Outer Marker Lights as all landings were made from the Eastern or coastwise end of the runway. Runway lights were a mixture of Contact and Drem Lights and these divided the strip into three equal lanes, each identified by different coloured marker lights, South Lane — Green, Centre Lane — White, and North Lane — Amber. This was designed to sort out the "Callers" into three categories; the procedure was to use the Amber Lane for badly shot up, damaged aircraft capable only of making a wheels-up landing, less badly damaged or partially-powered aircraft used the White Lane, while machines low on fuel but otherwise capable of flight touched down on the Green Lane.

Unusual equipment for an airfield were the numerous bulldozers, cranes and other items of heavy lifting equipment used for crash removal, all of which were to be fully employed over the months and years ahead.

Officially opened on 15th November, 1943, the runway had already played host to visitors before this date as by then nineteen aircraft, all in distress, had used the runway as a place of refuge. On 18th July, 1943, a U.S.A.F. B-17 Fortress approached the Suffolk coast, badly damaged and low on fuel, and its crew, seeing the newly constructed runway, put the ailing bomber down among the construction gear and empty barrels which had been scattered on the strip to prevent such an occurrence. Neither aircraft nor runway suffered further damage. This was to be the first of 4,115 aircraft to make emergency landings, 1,100 due to technical trouble, 995 suffering battle damage, 820 short of fuel and 1,200 due to bad weather, mainly fog at their home bases.

The airfield's official name was R.A.F. Woodbridge, but it was generally known to all and sundry as Sutton Heath. It was also mentioned in many official documents as Woodbridge E.L.G., Emergency Landing Ground. The first Commanding Officer was Wing Commander D. H. Burnside, D.F.C., who assumed command during September, 1943. During these early days there was insufficient accommodation for all the personnel and so until October they were housed at R.A.F. Martlesham Heath. Aerodrome defence personnel arrived on 30th October, 1943, when a detachment of the R.A.F. Regiment marched the five miles from the railway station at Woodbridge.

Right from the opening day a twenty-four-hour watch was maintained in the Control Tower and full W/T and R/T facilities were available. Short notice accommodation and messing was available for seventy-five aircrew, which was just as well as during the first fourteen days of operation fifty-five emergency landings were made.

What were the aircraft like that were destined to make use of Woodbridge? In the main they were "heavies" of R.A.F. Bomber Command and the daylight "heavies" of the U.S.A.A.F., and they made their calls basically at two distinct times. Late afternoon and early evening saw the battered arrivals of the American 8th Air Force, while from late evening through the dawn, survivors of the R.A.F.'s night battles over Occupied Europe crawled in.

When Woodbridge became operational the twin-engined medium/heavy bombers which had been the mainstay of Bomber Command's offensive excursions were playing their last parts. First of the new four-engined long-range heavies to enter service early in 1941 was the Short Stirling, bigger than anything else to date, many examples of this type operating from airfields in East Anglia. The Stirling had started life under a cloud as the Air Ministry specification to which it had been designed stipulated a wingspan of not more than 99 feet in order that the aircraft could be housed in the then existing 100 feet portal hangars. Many ingenious devices were employed to get the load performance called for, and the Stirling was easily recognized by its long box-like fuselage and tall stalky undercarriage. This aircraft was to be a very frequent visitor to Woodbridge, in many cases arriving in a style more befitting its flying boat sisters — wheels up and sliding along the runway, often on a bed of foam. Loved by the majority of its crews and respected for its

Early days at Sutton Heath, with three airmen outside their billet, a bell tent set in a sylvan glade. The bicycle was an essential piece of equipment because of the distance between sites.

fighter-like performance in the air but often dangerous antics near the ground, the Stirling was summed up by one skipper as the most expensive method devised to date of getting an undercarriage off the ground!

Following in the Stirling's wake came the Handley-Page Halifax. Powered by four Rolls-Royce Merlin liquid-cooled motors, as opposed to the Stirling's air-cooled Bristol Hercules, the rather angular Halifax operated mainly from airfields in Yorkshire under the command of No. 4 Group. Faster than the Stirling and capable of greater altitude, the Halifax underwent a major design change, new versions entering service during the autumn of 1943 with nose turret removed, Hercules air-cooled engines in place of Merlins and squared-up fins and rudders in place of the previously angled ones. Several Royal

Handley-Page Halifax I.
*Rolls-Royce (1971)
Ltd.*

Canadian Air Force squadrons operated the Halifax and as a consequence our colonial cousins were frequent visitors to the strip. Residents at the Woodbridge 'drome never stopped being amazed at the amount of punishment that the Halifax, or the "Halibag" as it was affectionately known, could take and the often terribly battered condition in which they arrived. As the Halifax's Yorkshire homes were furthest from the targets it was only to be expected that many would make emergency calls at Woodbridge, especially with "drying-out" fuel tanks.

Last of the R.A.F.'s four-engined bombers to enter service, the Avro Lancaster was the reincarnation of its designers' not-too-successful Manchester. Now powered by four Merlins, this was to be the most successful of the trio, and indeed of any bomber engaged in the Second World War. Capable in modified form of carrying a 22,000 lb bomb, the largest missile carried by any aircraft, the Lancaster in its standard guise could roar along at 275 m.p.h. at 15,000 feet, and over the months of operation became loved and trusted by its crews. Based mainly in Lincolnshire and Nottinghamshire and eventually comprising over 60% of Bomber Command's heavy bomber component, the

Lancaster by virtue of its numerical superiority was the most frequent visitor to Woodbridge.

The U.S.A.A.F. visitors, which usually called during daylight hours, were both aircraft powered by four air-cooled radial engines, the Boeing B-17 Fortress being a low-wing monoplane while the Consolidated B-24 Liberator was of the high-wing design with twin fins and rudders. Not capable of the bomb-load-carrying capabilities of the R.A.F. machines, they were however more heavily armed both in the number of guns carried and in the fact that these guns were of 0.5-inch calibre as opposed to the British 0.303-inch.

Rising almost daily in tremendous numbers from their East Anglian bases, they circled and formed up into formations and climbed out and up

Short Stirling, first of the four-engined heavy bombers.
Shorts

over the North Sea until tell-tale condensation trails marked their course over the Third Reich. There, in a hell of hot metal and frozen atmosphere, thousands of young men conducted a battle of a kind never before known to mankind, one in which the chances of survival were slim and the least that one could expect was to arrive back over the British Isles in some shape or other.

These then, in the main, were the machines which called only when in trouble, some leaving again under their own power while for many others the last journey was to the railway station at Melton.

Records show the circumstances in which aircraft made for the emergency airfield: The pilot of a U.S.A.A.F. Republic P-47 Thunderbolt fighter patrolling over Belgium discovered to his horror that his engine throttle linkage had jammed tight with the engine running at full throttle. Setting course for the British Isles, he arrived at considerable speed over the airfield and circled round at over 300 m.p.h. Making a long, fast landing approach, he failed at his first landing attempt, but made it the second time by shutting off his fuel supply on touch-down, still finishing up in the overshoot area, 4,000 yards from his landing spot.

Often the needs of the approaching disabled bomber were desperate and one hair-raising episode was recalled by ex-Flight Lieutenant Watling. While making an emergency landing in a Handley-Page Halifax he was about to touch down when another aircraft, landing in the adjacent lane, stumbled and veered across in front of the Halifax. Slamming the four throttle levers "through the gate"* the crew of the Halifax just managed to get enough power to enable their faltering aircraft to claw up and over, but only just over, the other bomber. Shutting the throttles again, they slammed the Halifax down hard on to the runway before they ran out of concrete.

Little more than a month after the airfield officially became operational there occurred a series of tragic incidents involving a force of Handley-Page Halifax bombers which led to modifications being made to the runway lighting system. The night of 17th December, 1943, was extremely hazy, with cloud base down to 300 feet. The Halifaxes had set out from their base at Gibraltar Farm, Tempsford, in Bedfordshire, to take supplies and agents to the Resistance Forces in occupied Eastern Europe, but heavy rain and very low cloud over the dropping zones led to the mission being aborted and they were recalled.

On arrival over the East Anglian coast the Halifax force received orders to divert to the new Emergency Landing Ground at Woodbridge, but when they arrived overhead the runway was hidden in haze. For some reason Ground Control were unable to contact the aircraft, and because of the dense ground mist the aircrews could not see either the runway or the Very lights that were fired from the ground. A further difficulty was that because of intense radio interference the aircrews were unable to use their Direction Finding equipment to fix their positions.

Eventually one Halifax managed to grope its way down through the murk to locate the strip and make a safe landing. It was the only one to do so. At 05.05 hours a second Halifax, DK.206 of No. 161 Squadron, trying to fly down to cloud base, crashed into the conifers of Tangham Forest at Capel St Andrew not far from the seaward end of the runway. Three crew died and three others were injured in the crash.

A few minutes later another Halifax Mk. V, LK.899, also of No. 161 Squadron, crashed into the River Deben at Bawdsey while making a low approach, one of the crew being killed and two others being badly injured. Then at 05.30 hours Halifax LL.115 of No. 138 Squadron attempted to break cloud base in order to locate the strip and plunged into trees at Capel Green with the loss of five crew killed and three injured.

Rescuers at the scene of this crash and that at Capel St Andrew were hampered by the large number of grenades and the amount of small arms

*Past the normal full throttle position, into the emergency slot.

ammunition scattered around, these being among the supplies which were to have been dropped to the Resistance.

At the same time that Halifax LL.115 crashed at Capel Green another Halifax Mk.V of No. 138 Squadron, LL.119, crashed into the sea close to the shore at Felixstowe after the crew had baled out. Fortunately all were picked up. Within a few minutes a third No. 138 Squadron aircraft, Halifax B.II LW.280, plunged into the sea half a mile off the Essex coast near Harwich, three of her crew being killed as they baled out just as the bomber hit the water.

The remaining Halifax was slightly more fortunate than most of its companions. LL.120, a Mark V of No. 161 Squadron, flew up the coast and eventually ditched in the sea off Skegness, Lincolnshire, at 05.45 hours. The crew all baled out and were all picked up, only one man being injured.

Halifaxes were not the only aircraft to be used on missions in connection with Special Operations Executive (S.O.E.). The late Squadron Leader Holmes, of Bradford, recalled the night when he made a frightening wheels-up landing at Woodbridge in a Stirling at the end of a long-range mission to Eastern Europe. Devoid of all electrical power and out of fuel, all four Hercules motors stopped as the aircraft approached over the threshold. The Stirling crunched down and slid along the runway before veering off the concrete and into the rough.

With the steadily increasing business, the station staff grew rapidly. By January, 1944, it had grown to 600 men, of whom 200 were R.A.F. Regiment personnel engaged on aerodrome defence duties which were considered particularly necessary because of the Station's proximity to the East Coast.

At this time the Station was not self-accounting, depending on Martlesham Heath both for that function and for the provision of Equipment Section facilities. The majority of the buildings were complete, however, and accommodation was available for a hundred and fifty visiting aircrew. A cinema was being built, and until it was completed films were shown in the Airmen's Dining Hall.

As the carcasses of wrecked aircraft slowly accumulated steps were taken to deal with them, a detachment from No. 54 Maintenance Unit at Newmarket taking up residence to look after this job. Work also began on the installation of the F.I.D.O. (Fog Investigation and Dispersal Organisation) equipment that was designed to clear fog from the runway.

Experiments with a system intended to assist returning aircraft to reach the safety of a clear runway on foggy autumn nights had been carried out on another East Anglian airfield, Lakenheath in West Suffolk, during September, 1943. The installation at Sutton Heath was the biggest of several F.I.D.O. installations completed in 1944.

The F.I.D.O. system consisted of large pipelines laid along either side of

119

the runway and carrying petrol under pressure which was burned in burners set at intervals along each pipe. The intense heat created by the burning fuel caused an updraught which dispersed the fog in the immediate vicinity of the runway. Extremely costly to operate, the system did prove successful in improving visibility from 100 yards to 2,000 yards, no mean feat.

The large quantities of fuel required were brought in railway tank wagons to a siding on the L.N.E.R. Ipswich-Lowestoft line at Dock Lane, Melton, from where a pipeline ran under the River Deben to a fuel store near the airfield. During one spell of foggy weather the F.I.D.O. system was burned continuously for nine hours, consuming 100,000 gallons of high octane petrol per hour. No doubt wartime motorists filling up with their meagre ration would have groaned at such statistics had they known of them.

A number of troubles were experienced with the system, one of them being clogging of the burner jets. A vast amount of oily black smoke was produced during the first few minutes of operation, until the system had heated up, and at times this could be even worse than the fog. Mr R. A. Cheetham, of Leigh, who served in Flying Control at Sutton Heath, re-members that on the first night F.I.D.O. was in operation fire engines from a considerable area of Suffolk rushed to the vicinity of the airfield as rumours spread of an extensive forest fire in Tangham Forest.

Becoming operational during June, 1944, the F.I.D.O. system was not used a great deal until the autumn, when it did prove effective. One foggy night in January, 1945, when a large force of bombers was out raiding Germany, more than a hundred of the aircraft made use of the installation to find their way down to a safe landing. In all some 1,200 landings were made with the aid of F.I.D.O., one of the last operational aircraft to make use of the system being an 8th U.S.A.A.F. B-24 Liberator which landed just before V.E. Day.

However useful it was, F.I.D.O. was fearsome in action and several ex-aircrew members have told the author how perturbed they were as they descended towards the leaping lines of flame. The result of a swing-off into the pipeline and burners would have been horrific. A by-product of F.I.D.O. was, of course, huge masses of superheated air which rose towards the approaching aircraft, often in a more or less uncontrollable condition as a result of battle damage. Aircraft were badly buffeted by the turbulence, and it required the full attention of the aircrew to keep the bucking bomber on its course.

During 1944 the runway lighting at Woodbridge was improved as a result of the unhappy experience with the Halifaxes the previous December. Further sodium and incandescent lamps were added in the lead-in area as well as additional approach beacon lights which stretched from the eastern end of the runway to within a mile of the coast at Orford.

Visitors arrived in increasing numbers as the day and night bomber

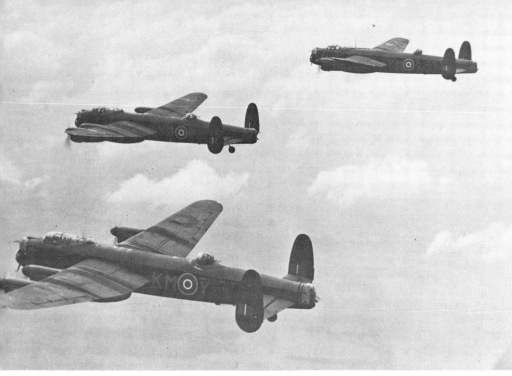

Avro Lancaster B1s of No. 44 (Rhodesia) Squadron based at Waddington, Lincolnshire, on their way to the target. Many such aircraft made use of the Emergency Landing Ground at the end of their mission.   *British Aerospace*

offensives gained momentum, and from some fifty-seven emergency landings during December, 1944, and sixty during January, 1945, numbers grew to seventy-two in February, 1945. Forty-eight of them were American aircraft returning to their East Anglian Bases. One that did not make it was Liberator B-24 serialled 42-7574 of the 446th Bomb Group based at Flixton, near Bungay, in Suffolk. Badly damaged, it was approaching the E.L.G. at 16.55 hours on 24th February, 1945, when on crossing the coast the pilot, Lieutenant Cecil T. Miller, ordered his crew to bale out. Nine men left the stricken aircraft, but before the captain could leave it the Liberator plunged into the ground and blew up at Sternfield, near Saxmundham.

Visitors of an unwelcome nature also called, although their arrival on the scene was not always intended. Many enemy aircraft whose allotted target was the London area unloaded their cargoes in the district while on their way back to their home bases. This was the case at 20.40 hours on 29th January, 1944, when a Junkers Ju.88 jettisoned ten 50kg. high explosive bombs and 561 incendiaries on the area when attacked by a Beaufighter of No. 68 Squadron. The enemy eventually crashed at Barham, on the other side of Ipswich. On 4th February high explosives and incendiaries fell at Wantisden, Butley and

Eyke, and ten days later another shower of missiles was jettisoned by a London-bound bomber. Then on 21st February, a single enemy bomber dropped six 50kg high explosive bombs and 597 incendiaries, the latter the contents of an AB.1000 incendiary container, at Boyton and Hollesley. No casualties or damage resulted from any of these incidents.

March, 1944, saw the arrival of 130 aircraft availing themselves of Woodbridge's giant runway facilities. One particularly busy session was during the early hours of 25th March, when within the space of twenty-eight minutes nine badly damaged bombers were brought in and removed from their resting places by the handling parties.

With almost everything else now available, the one commodity in short supply was water, the one well on the site being unable to supply the Station's needs. A fleet of lorries was engaged in making runs to the town of Woodbridge for liquid supplies, but towards the end of March the well was deepened and adequate supplies obtained. As a result baths and showers were available again for short periods daily, after being closed for three weeks.

All Fool's Day, 1st April, 1944, brought an intruder believed to have been a Messerschmitt Me.410 twin-engined fighter which attempted to make a surprise call on the E.L.G. but dropped its H.E. bombs at nearby Chillesford instead. These caused no casualties and very little damage.

The tempo increased during April, the total for that month amounting to 159, with one notable incident occurring on the 23rd when at 03.55 hours Avro Lancaster LS-W skidded to a splintering belly landing opposite the Control Tower. To say that it was badly damaged would be an under-statement, as it arrived with only two of its four Merlins running, two gun

A North American P-47D Thunderbolt, 42-76211 of the 359th Fighter Squadron, after it had crashed on 26th February, 1944, killing the pilot, Lieutenant Cotter.   *U.S.A.F./Mactaggart*

turrets knocked out, all tailplane controls, undercarriage and flaps useless, and three of its crew dead. The wreckage was removed from the runway in fourteen minutes—no mean feat!

Another casualty was a Handley-Page Halifax B.III of No. 433 Squadron, Royal Canadian Air Force, which came in with almost 64 square feet of its starboard wing in tatters and all its navigational equipment smashed after a raid on Karlsruhe.

Not all the crashes were actually on the strip, as many aircraft came to grief as they approached Woodbridge or got into trouble while flying in the district. At 10.40 hours on 26th April, 1944, a P-47 Thunderbolt of the 356th Fighter Group from Martlesham Heath crashed in flames on Bromeswell Golf Course, killing the pilot, Second Lieutenant R. B. Warren. A few weeks earlier, on 8th March, a similar aircraft of the 56th Fighter Group at Holton, near Halesworth, had crashed near "The Lodge", Hollesley, but the pilot, a Pole, Captain Mike Cladych, had baled out and landed safely.

Ever-increasing traffic necessitated more men to deal with it, and by mid-1944 the Station Roll stood at over 800. This was increased when a detachment of the U.S.A.A.F. took up residence to deal with their "lame ducks" and wrecks. Another detachment arrived at this time, namely the Bomb Ballistics Unit (B.B.U.), their work being carry out trials with large bombs. They were accommodated in bell tents alongside the runway, a not too hospitable environment as at this time several forest fires broke out in the trees bordering the strip, all the Station staff being mustered to assist the National Fire Service in quelling the flames.

June with its longer days saw no-let up in activities, the month's tally being 147. It was at this time that a new arrival, the V1 flying bomb or "Buzz Bomb" as it was sometimes called, made its noisy presence known in East Anglia. It is said that one was sighted by a Control Officer at Woodbridge who, not recognising it for what it was, gave it permission to land by signalling a Green on his Aldis lamp. Fortunately the robot bomb did not heed his instructions.

An incident which showed how tragedy always lurked so close occurred on 14th June, when a 493rd Bomb Group Liberator, 41-29569 based at Debach, Suffolk, circled the strip with one dead engine. It was in the circuit when it suddenly rolled over on to its back and crashed at Melton, where it burned out with the loss of its ten-man crew.

It was during the dawn half-light on 22nd June that a fully bombed up, badly damaged Lancaster which had been mauled by a German night fighter made an unheralded touch-down in the Green Lane. Because of brake failure it careered across the strip and slithered to a smashing standstill on the south side of the Amber lane. The bomber's crew and No. 54 M.U. personnel were hastily warned by the Tannoy of other impending dangers, and they ran for their lives as a B-17 Fortress of the U.S.A.F. touched down on the Green runway. Veering across the strip after touchdown, it smashed into the wreckage of the Lancaster, cutting it completely in half with its starboard wing, before coming to a standstill with a collapsed undercarriage in the centre of the Amber runway. The Green lane was still fortunately semi-clear as another Lancaster with almost empty fuel tanks asked for and was given permission to land. Its undercarriage crumpled on touchdown and amid a shower of sparks and rending metal the bomber slowly spun round and round and ground to a halt in the Green lane. As the Control Officer prepared to close the airfield to further traffic, another Lancaster in the same predicament was forced to make for the Green runway. Passing low over the wreckage of the other bombers, it made a hurried landing on the remainder of the strip. All this happened within less than a quarter of an hour, and not one person was injured.

In the vicinity of Sutton Heath was a dummy aerodrome situated on Hollesley Heath. Plans had originally been made during 1939 to construct decoy airfields which would have to use visibly acceptable aircraft mock-ups, buildings and installations situated in authentic surroundings. Their purpose was to attract enemy attention and draw off attacks from the real site, and, enemy photography being of an extremely high standard, the mock-ups had to look authentic indeed. As only very few obsolete or unserviceable aircraft were available for this purpose, other sources of supply had to be arranged, and finally those masters of deception from the film industry took on the task.

Appearing most realistic and lifelike from both high and low level observation, and with correct shadow appearances, the dummies were turned out in considerable quantities. Hurricanes, Blenheims, Spitfires, Battles and Wellingtons were all impersonated, all the imitation aircraft bearing correct markings for known squadrons so that their identity could be checked on, leading to even more confusion in the enemy camp. Ingenuity ran wild in their design and construction as they were completely collapsible and several "aircraft" types could be loaded on one lorry for movement from one site to another as the squadron made its daily or weekly moves. This movement was frequently carried out in order to give the enemy photographic interpreter a wild goose chase and a greatly enhanced idea of the R.A.F.'s strength.

Many of the decoy sites were so authentic that a resident party had to be stationed there to warn off Allied pilots intent on landing on he new 'drome, especially at night when the flarepath was lit and the decoy appeared to be all ready for business. The flarepath lights were placed closer than normal in order to give an enemy pilot a false illusion of height. Shelters were of course provided for the residents of the site, most desirable when raiders decided to rearrange the layout of the site.

The enemy was indeed interested, as was made evident by the events of

23rd June, 1944, when a Junkers Ju.188E coded F6 + JL, Werk No. 281620, took off at 21.00 hours from Soesterberg, near Utrecht in the Netherlands, for a flight over the North Sea and East Anglia. Belonging to a reconnaissance unit, 1/(F)122, the aircraft carried a crew of five and was equipped with two N r B 50 × 30 cm night cameras which were used in conjunction with BLC 50 flash bombs. The crew members were Leutnant Kasper (pilot), Oberleutnant Hopka (observer), Unteroffizier Marweiser (wireless operator), Obergefreiter Verkhausen (gunner) and Unteroffizier Scheel (engineer-gunner). The Ju.188 was located by British radar when it was some fifty miles out at sea, heading west at 22,000 feet. As it overflew eight-tenths clouds it apparently became lost. Heading towards it was a De Havilland Mosquito N.F. XVII, HK. 257 of No. 25 Squadron from Coltishall, Norfolk, flown by Wing Commander Wight-Boycott, D.S.O., who was engaged on a practice sortie over the area. An experienced night fighter pilot, the Mosquito's captain stalked the intruder and closed in as the Ju.188 crossed the Suffolk coast near Orfordness. The night fighter fired four short bursts and the Ju.188 caught fire immediately and dived away to port, breaking up as it fell. The main wreckage crashed at Wantisden Heath at 00.28 hours.

Rescuers found four of the crew dead, two of them hit by the fighter's 20mm cannon shells. Twenty-two-year-old Willi Scheel, who had been hurled from the plunging wreckage and parachuted down, landed with only minor injuries. He gave himself up at 06.00 hours at Butley, where he was collected by Military Police from Woodbridge who also guarded the wreckage.

On examination of the Ju.188's remains, it was discovered that the camera equipment carried was of great interest to the R.A.F., as this was the first time that cameras of this type had been found in crashed Luftwaffe aircraft in the United Kingdom. It was obvious that the Ju.188's objective was to obtain infra-red photographs and radar pictures of the decoy airfield at Hollesley as part of its mission. It is most interesting that the enemy aircraft was shot down using radar by an aircraft from the same squadron that when based at Martlesham early in the war was the first unit to destroy an enemy machine using this device.

On 24th June a single enemy raider dropped seven H.E. bombs on the nearby village of Sutton, fortunately without causing casualties or damage. Just before the attack a Junkers Ju.188 had been shot down by a Mosquito night fighter at Wantisden and it is thought that the latter attacker might have mistaken the burning Luftwaffe bomber's wreckage for its target. Another raider called and left visiting cards in the form of H.E. bombs which fell dangerously close, the nearest only 300 yards from the giant fuel tanks containing almost one million gallons of high octane petrol for the newly installed F.I.D.O. system. Later on the same night at 22.40 hours a V1 impacted on marshland near Shottisham Hall, this being the first of the type

The Junkers JU.88G-1 night fighter sits on the apron at Sutton Heath on the morning after its unexpected arrival. Its radar aerials on nose and wings can be clearly seen.

to reach the vicinity of the E.L.G, and the fourth to reach Suffolk. Only minor damage to some farm buildings resulted.

July brought many incidents and a further increase in personnel, the roll call now totalling 1,100 men, which caused severe accommodation problems. Many residents were glad that it was summer as they were housed in bell tents among the trees. It was an all-male establishment, no W.A.A.F. personnel ever being stationed there. When circumstances allowed the luxury of a Station Dance, female partners had to be imported from neighbouring stations. Nevertheless, these functions were famed and still well remembered with nostalgia by many people now scattered around the world.

Sometimes in the midst of war fate plays strange tricks. So it was on the night of 13th July, 1944, when a Junkers Ju.88 G-1 twin-engined heavy night fighter took off from Volkel in Holland on a bomber interception patrol which should have taken it towards North-west Germany and eventually to a landing at an aerodrome near Berlin. This aircraft was unusual in that it was fitted with a Ju.188 tail unit; more important, it carried the latest FUG 220 Lichtenstein SN2 interceptor radar and FUG 227 Flensburg homing device, both of them designed to be unaffected by the "Window" dropped by the R.A.F. bombers. Like other night fighters of its kind, it was also fitted with long-range fuel tanks designed to enable it to carry out extended patrols across the track of outgoing and returning Allied bomber streams.

After the Ju.88 had been flying for some time defects appeared in its navigational and wireless telegraphy systems. In spite of desperate efforts on the part of the crew to restore contact with their base the aircraft was soon completely lost. The crew became worried about shortage of fuel, but as the gauges showed the tanks to be nearly empty they saw the faint landing lights of what they took to be a friendly airfield, probably, they thought, the Luftwaffe base at Venlo on the Dutch-German border.

At Sutton Heath the Duty Crew was going about its work in the darkness of early morning, as Mr G. G. Youell, of Mitcham, Surrey, recalls:

"It was a misty, dark night, late, about 1.30 a.m. or thereabouts, and the Duty Crew had only just seen a Short Stirling bomber off the runway and had parked it close by the Duty Crew Hut. The ground crew lads went indoors, while inside the Stirling its crew were collecting their things together, when a call from Control sent the Duty Crew out into the night again for another aircraft.

"As they switched on the guide lights of a 15cwt. van, the aircraft which had just landed with its navigation and landing lights switched on rolled down the runway towards them, turned into a hard-standing and parked next to the Stirling, from which the crew were just emerging by the rear door near the tailplane.

"The first thing they saw was the German insignia on the aircraft next to them, and they beat a hasty retreat back up the bomber's fuselage and attempted to start up the four motors on the aircraft's internal batteries. Their first thought was that they had landed in German-occupied territory.

"The other aircraft's crew also thought that they were on home ground, but too late they realised their mistake. They were overcome by the Duty Crew, who fortunately had a Sergeant amateur boxer leading them into the fray."

That amateur boxer was Sergeant K. E. Clifton, D.F.M., who had recognised the Ju.88 for what it was. He parked the 15cwt. truck in front of the German aircraft to prevent any attempt to move it and then led his crew into the fray. Wrenching open the door beneath the front fuselage, the Sergeant took quick action to counter attempts by the German crew to destroy the aircraft's log and code books. The sudden opening of the door caused the pilot to fall out and he, says Mr Youell, came off second best in the ensuing scuffle with the amateur boxer.

"The Stirling's crew, who were lost anyway, took some convincing that it was England, but some good Anglo-Saxon swearwords eventually had them convinced that the natives were indeed friendly," says Mr Youell. "An American interpreter was found to interrogate the German crew, and the next day the Ju.88 was repainted with R.A.F. markings and flown off by a Farnborough test pilot accompanied by, I think, six Spitfires."

The capture of this aircraft was considered so important that several high-ranking officers, including Air Marshal Sorley, Air Vice-Marshal Harrison, Air Commodore Kirkpatrick and Air Commodore Gayford, arrived at Woodbridge at first light to inspect it. Top technical experts also arrived to examine the machine before it was flown off to Farnborough for detailed examination. Farnborough used the captured Ju.88 to the full. It carried the R.A.F. serial number TP.170 and the yellow P in a circle on the fuselage denoting a prototype until it was written off in a forced landing.

The experts were intensely interested in the equipment on board the aircraft which was being used, unknown to the Allies, by Luftwaffe night fighter pilots to home on to Bomber Command heavies as they flew over enemy territory. The Flensburg apparatus was able to pick up signals from the bombers' "Monica", a set which was intended to warn bomber crews of attacking aircraft coming up astern. As a result of what was learnt from the captured Ju.88 urgent modifications were made to the Allied equipment, and bomber losses were lessened in consequence. After examination of the FUG

The Junkers Ju. 88G-1 after it had been flown from Sutton Heath to Farnborough, its Luftwaffe markings replaced by standard British roundels. Its R.A.F. serial TP.190 can be seen on the rear fuselage.

220 apparatus, R.A.F. "boffins" devised a new type of "Window" and within a few days of the Ju.88's arrival at Woodbridge R.A.F. bombers were enabled to venture forth in comparatively greater safety. At the same time a new radio countermeasures device named "Piperack" was fitted to the Norfolk-based aircraft of No. 100 Group with the object of putting added clutter on the enemy defence radar screens. Eventually "Monica" was replaced by another device which gave rearward warning without being used by the enemy.

The arrival of that Ju.88 in the early hours marked a highlight at Woodbridge, but to the men working there it was no more than one incident among many that occurred in a very busy period. On 16th July at 10.00 hours Boeing B-17 Fortress 42-39912 of the 385th Bomb Group from Great Ashfield, Suffolk, tore its way through the trees 1,200 yards short of the runway at the Capel St Andrew end, but all the crew escaped unhurt. Two days later at 14.20 hours a Martlesham Heath based 256th Fighter Group P-47 Thunderbolt 42-26565 collided with another P-47 while carrying out mock attacks and crashed in Tangham Forest, its pilot, First Lieutenant S. J. Green, being killed. The other P-47 managed a hurried landing at Woodbridge with a badly damaged propeller and an even more badly vibrating engine. Another V1 passed over the strip later in the day, and a few anxious moments were spent until it had reverberated its way through the E.L.G. airspace and finally impacted at Iken.

D-Day, 6th June, had brought an increase in customers and the tally for July was 191 aircraft, which included a record thirty-eight four-engined bombers landing within a space of fifty-five minutes!

Many deeds of heroism were enacted as aircraft struggled towards Woodbridge, one such incident occurring on the night of 28th/29th July, 1944. Badly damaged by flak over Hamburg, a Lancaster of No. 156 (Pathfinder) Squadron captained by the Squadron Commander, Squadron Leader H. F. Slade, an Australian, released its markers and then dived out of control towards the blazing city. Ignoring orders from the captain to bale out, the crew managed to get it back on to an even keel, although aileron control was only one-tenth of what it should have been. It was only by juggling the fuel in the aircraft's tanks that trim was maintained. Gradually losing height all the way over the North Sea, the almost uncontrollable Lancaster made for the Suffolk coast, which it crossed at 1,500 feet, almost at the end of its tether. Slade summoned his last reserves of strength in order to make the emergency landing, which was successful, the only damage incurred being to the already crippled bomber.

Often the long runway saw the unfortunate end of an aircraft, as in the case of Lancaster ND.806 of No. 166 Squadron, which crashed and burned after struggling home, having been engaged in a series of running fights almost the whole way back across the North Sea. On another occasion a Boeing

Fortress, badly damaged by heavy anti-aircraft fire, arrived over Woodbridge and made a high-speed landing, utilising the whole length of the massive runway. Inspection later revealed a gap sixteen feet by six feet under the centre fuselage adjacent to the wing main spar; another hole in the fuselage measured eight feet by six feet. If this was not enough, over fifty per cent of the surface of the starboard wing was missing, as well as other assorted damage. This Fortress was scrapped on the spot.

Another U.S.A.A.F. four-engined bomber, a Consolidated B-24 Liberator, swung badly on touch-down and slewed off the concrete to run into the newly installed F.I.D.O. pipework. Its port wing sheered off some young conifers while the starboard one smashed into the Airfield Control caravan, from which the Controller, Sergeant Christmas, escaped uninjured but badly shocked. Still careering along, it then beat-up a Forestry Commission light truck that was parked near the caravan. Swinging round once again, the aircraft continued its career of destruction, the port wing severing the body off a contractor's coach, while the remains of the starboard wing demolished a steel loudspeaker (Tannoy) tower. What was left of the aircraft then stood on its nose in the middle of one of the dispersal loops. Out of all this chaos the only casualties were the Forestry Commission truck driver, who suffered superficial cuts and bruises, and the shocked Controller.

Incidents were still on the increase. During August the thousandth emergency landing was made and by the end of the month the total was 1,144. The abnormally wet summer added to the difficulties suffered by returning Allied bombers and fighters as they struggled to reach safety after many a desperate ordeal over the North Sea. One such casualty was Lancaster LL.697 of No. 514 Squadron which sustained a direct hit by a bomb dropped from another Lancaster flying above it and lost its nose section, together with the bomb aimer. With a howling gale roaring in through the gaping front fuselage and all his instruments bar the altimeter out of action the Lancaster's pilot, Warrant Officer Beaton, nursed the stricken bomber back across the North Sea, escorted by another aircraft from the same squadron. Both eventually made safe landings on the strip.

Anxiety mounted just before 20.00 hours on 18th August, when a V1 approached the strip flying at under 1,000 feet, but it passed over safely and crashed at Great Bealings, near Woodbridge, making a crater 28 feet wide by 14 feet deep. Twelve houses were damaged and one man slightly hurt.

September saw the arrival of no fewer than 266 aircraft, but as the station strength had now increased to over 1,100 men it was well staffed in all departments. Visiting aircrew accommodation was adequate for such a number, but this was not to be the case for long as the winter months would bring in many more visitors.

Excitement was intense around midday on 12th September, when a badly damaged B-24 Liberator circled near the Suffolk coast as its pilot ordered his crew to parachute to safety. Having seen them clear of the aircraft he engaged "George", the automatic pilot system, and pointed the bomber towards the sea before making his own escape. Apparently the B-24 did not relish the idea of a watery grave, because as it crossed the coast seawards it turned through 180 degrees and headed back inland on its original course.

As if piloted by human hand it appeared over the airfield, where for the next ten minutes it proceeded to indulge in a series of steep stalled turns over the runway. These strenuous manoeuvres were too much for the already

Men of No. 54 Maintenance Unit and of the Bomb Ballistics Unit photographed in front of and on top of a visting Lancaster, probably to the dismay of its crew who would have to explain to their Chief Technical Officer the loss of paint on the upper wing surfaces.   *Peter Rowland*

weakened structure and the tailplane and rear fuselage broke off and, appropriately enough, fell into the Salvage Compound, while what was left dived into the runway, the four 1,200 h.p. Pratt and Whitney 14-cylinder radial engines breaking through the concrete and burying themselves five feet down.

After 1st September, 1944, the Germans mounted a V1 flying bomb campaign against East Anglian targets by air-launching these reaction-jet-propelled missiles from Heinkel 111 K bombers. Many of these terror weapons passed over the area. One such missile, air-launched off the Suffolk coast, crashed in a farmyard at Capel St Andrew, causing severe damage to the farm buildings and nearby cottages; fortunately only three people were slightly hurt. The following day, at 05.00 hours another V1 crashed into a tree at Sutton and the resultant blast caused widespread damage to nearby houses, but no casualties. Nine days later, at 05.20 hours another V1 plunged into the ground at Hollesley, where it caused considerable damage to one house and minor disturbance to twelve others.

On 2nd December, 1944, at 07.35 hours the V1's successor, the V2 high-altitude rocket, arrived at Poplar Farm, Ramsholt, ahead of its sonic boom, but apart from a large crater in open farmland and minor damage to farm buildings, the enemy's effort had been in vain. Sixteen days later another air-launched V1 came to earth at Shottisham, close to the boundary with Sutton, but only two houses were slightly damaged. It is interesting to note that the air-launched flying bombs were despatched around daybreak, probably to assist the Heinkel 111 crews with navigation, but it must have put them in greater peril from patrolling Mosquito fighters, as the Heinkel's performance was greatly impaired by the V1 slung beneath the centre section. Later reports showed that the Heinkel's top speed of 258 m.p.h. was reduced to under 200 m.p.h. by the drag of its passenger. Several launching aircraft were also lost by the temperamental behaviour of the V1s pulse-jet motor, which had a tendency to explode when being ignited. The launching aircraft, Heinkel 111's of the subtype H.22, served with III/KG.3 based at Gilze-Rijen in Holland.

One of these missiles dropped into the village of Capel St Andrew at 06.15 hours on 12th January, 1945, sliding to a stop near the front door of Mr Glading's Capel Green Farm, fortunately without detonating. It had been winged by anti-aircraft fire from a local gunsite manned by the City of London Regiment, R.A. This missile turned out to be the best example so far in captivity.

First person on the scene was the farm bailiff from nearby Home Farm, Mr W. Meadows, who immediately evacuated the Glading family from their home. Urgent calls to the Bomb Disposal squad brought along Captain H. J. Hunt as the Defusing Officer, with Captain G. Tyson as his assistant, and Captain C. Meadows, who was an expert on X-ray photography. They found that the V1 had made a long flat approach when gliding to earth and a very smooth landing had resulted, with the deadly nose section held high and cushioned in deep mud.

Captain Hunt's instructions were that the missile was to be X-rayed before defusing in order to ascertain the fuse type and also to find out if it contained any new and unknown devices or if it was booby-trapped. Intelligence reports showed up the fact that German fuses were usually perfect and that something untoward must have happened to this particular missile and its detonating mechanism. Usually the explosive content weighed-in at about 850 kgs (1,870 lb) and the firing mechanism comprised a highly sensitive electric impact fuse connected to the switches in the nose, an all-way mechanical impact fuse and sometimes a clock fuse, the latter designed to destroy the missile should the other two fail to detonate. The bomb was almost 28½ feet (8.6 m) long with a wing span of 17½ feet (5.2 m), and the propulsion unit was 11¼ feet (3.4 m) long.

The Disposal Squad encountered great difficulty in attempts to X-ray the fuses as they were forced to stand in ooze almost up to their waists, and in such conditions keeping a footing was arduous. After ascertaining that the nose fuse had smashed they decided it was imperative to remove the bomb from the muddy site. Requests for assistance were made to Sutton Heath, but before the necessary tractor and equipment arrived several anxious minutes were spent as large low-flying aircraft passed over on their way into the crash drome. Their engines caused alarming vibrations, the effect of which on the missile's fuses was not known. A steel cable was bent on to the tractor's drawbar and passed round a nearby tree, so that the tractor and its driver could work from behind the farmhouse and would have a little protection should the missile detonate. The ooze sucked hard at the missile and would not release it to the tractor's gentle pull, so as a last resort it was decided to give it a jerk in order to prise it from the clinging mud. This resulted in the cable snapping, but when a heavier one was substituted the missile came free.

It was now possible to X-ray the fuses, but before further work could proceed, Captain Hunt had to send a car to Ipswich Hospital, 20 miles distant, to obtain a glass fountain pen filler as used for eye-drops. This was needed to place a liquid solution of plaster of Paris inside the fuse mechanism; after a short time it would solidify and prevent the fuse operating. When rendered completely safe, the explosive content was removed and the casing sent to the U.S.A. for evaluation purposes. It was estimated that had the missile exploded on impact it would have completely cleared an area of 400 yards square.

Back at the strip, continuous heavy rain had waterlogged the airfield during October, 1944. The water-laden runway surface to some extent suppressed the fire hazard, but it also added to the problems of the sliding and slithering disabled bombers as they endeavoured to slow up, often without brakes or flaps. It is reported that one aircraft used the whole length of the strip plus the overshoot area in order to stop, no doubt with a greatly perspiring crew aboard. The weather conditions also hampered the transport to and from the site of personnel who were billeted at Bentwaters, another airfield being constructed about five miles away. Halifaxes appeared to be allergic to Woodbridge; on 12th October, a Mark VII, NP.738 of No. 432 (Canadian) Squadron, crashed at Manor Cottages, Hollesley, and was completely wrecked, its tailplane breaking off and lying in a nearby road.

In the autumn of 1944 the Station gained a new Commanding Officer, Wing Commander P. J. McGlin, D.F.C., taking over from Wing Commander

Burnside, who had been in command since the Station opened. Wing Commander Burnside was posted to be Squadron Commander of No. 193 Squadron.

Lancaster B.III, ND.453 coded FZ-D, was caught by German flak over Gelsenkirchen on Friday, 6th October, 1944, after it had delivered its bombs. Part of the tailplane of this veteran No. 635 Squadron bomber was shot away and two of its Merlin engines rendered inoperative. The chances of Flying Officer G. A. Thorne and his crew reaching their Downham Market base appeared very thin, but they set course for home and eventually reached the North Sea. While still maintaining height the wireless operator transmitted a "Mayday" signal so that Air Sea Rescue units could get a fix on them should

The Avro Lancaster I was a frequent caller at Sutton Heath, often arriving in severely damaged condition or on the last pints of fuel. This example is fitted with H2S radar in the bulge beneath the rear fuselage.

the need arise to ditch. Luck was with them, as the two remaining Merlins continued to function and the navigator gave the pilot a course for Wood-bridge.

Gradually losing height all the way home across the dark inhospitable North Sea, they crossed the Suffolk coast at only 500 feet and then began to lose height rapidly near Ipswich, where the Lancaster narrowly missed a run of high tension transmission lines. Then one of the grossly overworked engines gave up, and the bomber began an uncontrollable yawing motion. Under these conditions Flying Officer Thorne had no option but to put the bomber into a shallow glide, cut the remaining engine and hope for the best. At 06.20 hours, ND.453 smashed into a stubble field 200 yards from Bussock House, Shottisham. The tail unit was torn off by electric cables and came to rest in a ditch, while the main part of the wreckage burst into flames, with the aircraft's flares and ammunition adding to the conflagration. Flying Officer Thorne was knocked unconscious but five of the crew, shaken, cut and bruised, managed to scramble from the blazing wreck, dragging the unconscious pilot with them. Unfortunately the wireless operator was trapped in the wreck and died in the inferno. ND.453 had logged 338 hours of hazardous operational flying in the shell-torn skies over Germany.

Two days later another Lancaster, ME.787 of No. 619 Squadron, dropped down through broken cloud on a dark Suffolk night, having located the airfield after an extremely hazardous journey from the Ruhr. This aircraft only carried one crew member, Squadron Leader Parnell. He had ordered his crew to leave the stricken bomber by parachute, and had then managed to keep the unstable machine, which was losing height rapidly, in the air as far as Woodbridge. Burning well in the bomb bay and lower fuselage, the Lancaster came straight in and slithered to a standstill with only one of its four Merlin engines turning.

Life can be very insecure in wartime, and it certainly was for the crew of a No. 100 Squadron Lancaster which, having reached the safety of the strip with almost empty fuel tanks, refuelled and made ready to return to its home base. Roaring down the runway, devoid of bombload but heavy with fuel, it suffered complete loss of engine power, stalled and struck a building where it exploded in a gigantic welter of fire. The crew all died. It is almost unbelievable that this accident was the first at Woodbridge to result in fatalities.

Medical staff were on duty round the clock, and as many of the aircraft arriving carried wounded aircrew theirs was almost a runway-side vigil to minister to those in dire need of their services. During the first year of operations the Station Sick Quarters treated 570 casualties, while in the same period 2,719 aircraft had been forced to avail themselves of the airfield's facilities. Some 306 landings were made during November, 1944, many of them with the aid of F.I.D.O.

Being struck by bombs released from another aircraft flying above was always an operational hazard. A Lancaster of No. 514 Squadron based at Waterbeach, Cambridgeshire, suffered this treatment during November, being struck by four large bombs. One hit the port outer Merlin engine, another glanced off the port inner, the third registered a direct hit on the fuselage, penetrating it near the vital structure of the wing main spar, while the fourth hit the starboard outer engine. These hits reduced parts of the Lancaster almost to wreckage, but the pilot and his crew struggled to get the flying scrapheap to Sutton Heath where they managed to get it down to earth. The bombs, although fused, had not fallen far enough to become armed and therefore had acted only as giant sledge-hammers on the unfortunate aircraft's structure.

On 27th November another Lancaster from the same squadron sought the long runway after being engaged in a daylight raid on Cologne. It was badly damaged by flak but the crew decided to press on, bombed their target and then set course for home. The damage sustained made the aircraft extremely difficult to fly and Flight Lieutenant Pilcher, the captain, was forced to lash the control column to part of the cockpit structure in order to hold the controls in a central position and maintain straight and level flight. Wounded crewmen had to be attended and without doubt the immense length of the emergency runway was a more than welcome sight to the fatigued crew as they made a grinding slide to a halt on its surface.

An unusual aircraft type to make a forced landing was a Boeing B-17 Fortress in R.A.F. markings belonging to No. 217 (Special Duties) Squadron operating from Oulton in Norfolk. This was one of the American aircraft specially equipped for Radio Countermeasures duties and belonged to the famous No. 100 Group.

Station strength increased again during December, 1944, the roll call now being 1,200 men. It was boosted even more when a detachment arrived from No. 140 Squadron, a special duties squadron based at Methwold, Norfolk. Woodbridge now became, among other things, an operational station.

Even on Christmas Day the pace hardly slackened, as on that festive occasion several aircraft arrived, and the cooks had to squeeze out another 70 Christmas dinners for the visitors. A wartime observer, Mr Donald Smith, of Ipswich, who was later to become a pilot, visited the site on this day as an Air Training Corps Cadet. He recalls being astonished by the activity taking place, and his log records a total of forty-three emergency landings during the afternoon, many of them Lancasters, Halifaxes, Fortresses, Liberators and Mosquitoes as well as an assortment of fighter types.

As the majority of emergency landings were of the wheels-up variety, mobile cranes and bulldozers were always on hand at the side of the runway to clear the wreckage away. A wonderful efficiency was apparent in the way that the many incidents were cleared and assistance given to the troubled crews. As the days, weeks and months passed the mountains of wreckage, one R.A.F. and the other U.S.A.F., were fed almost daily by the bulldozers. What an Eldorado they would have made for present-day preservation enthusiasts!

Messing was always an unknown factor and the late Mr Douglas Pettit, who served on the catering staff, recalled that the cookhouse staff worked a twenty-four-hour shift. A phenomenal number of breakfasts would be needed on a busy early morning to satisfy the needs of hungry aircrews, based all over the British Isles but, it seemed, all eating at Woodbridge. To illustrate this point, one night in January, 1945, some 950 aircrew arrived for breakfast during a two-and-a-half-hour period, a massive order for any Catering Officer. Hot meals were available round the clock, but for many it was only a temporary stop as after refuelling, a between-flight check, and maybe a few temporary repairs, they were off again, homeward bound.

Frequent visitors to Sutton Heath were North American P-51 Mustangs such as this one, 413316 "Mildred", coded G.4-C, which was based at Leiston in Suffolk. This photograph was taken some time after D-Day, as is evident by the black and white "invasion" stripes on mainplane and fuselage.   *Mr Peter Barker*

The New Year 1945 came in cold, but the activity was far from cool because January proved to be a record month, 554 aircraft making use of Woodbridge. Heavy snow and ice with attendant fog made many homeward-bound bombers divert to the E.L.G. and for several nights the F.I.D.O. installation blazed a path through the murk.

The 13th February was an unfortunate day for a 375th Fighter Group P-51 Mustang based at Leiston. Climbing into a snowstorm, the pilot lost control and the aircraft crashed at Butley, where it burned out, the pilot dying in the wreck.

The weather improved during the latter part of February, and this showed up in the monthly reports as the number of visitors had fallen to 376. However, they still came. Limping in over the coast at 10.48 hours on the 1st February, B-17 Fortress 43-37509 of the 398th Bomb Group based at Nuthampstead failed to make the strip and crash-landed a quarter of a mile from Duck Corner, Hollesley, with three of its crew injured.

A notable casualty was a Lancaster on its way home from a raid on Dortmund whose pilot had discovered, while over the North Sea, that he had undercarriage trouble. Arriving over Woodbridge, he went into the circuit in bad shape and even worse visibility and with only fifteen minutes' fuel left in the tanks, but the airfield's searchlights and intense sodium lights enabled the pilot to orientate himself and make a safe landing in the South lane. When all seemed to be going well and 400 yards of the landing run had been made, the bomber suddenly swung through 180 degrees and finished up straddled across the North lane. Inspection later revealed that during the course of its homeward flight the Lancaster had been intercepted by a Luftwaffe night fighter and while carrying out violent evasive manoeuvres, a 1,000 lb bomb which had failed to release had suddenly broken loose and thrashed around in the bomb bay. This had caused considerable damage to the hydraulic pipelines which ran along the inside of the fuselage wall, and had in turn caused the malfunctioning of the undercarriage as the bomb swung about during the landing run.

Duck Corner, Hollesley, was the scene of another incident on 1st March, 1945, when a 392nd Bomb Group B-24 Liberator, 44-10495, from Wendling in Norfolk crash-landed. The crew all survived the impact although the aircraft was wrecked. Three days later a Halifax B.III, NP.931 of No. 640 Squadron from Leconfield, Yorkshire, was making for the strip on three engines when at 00.20 hours it plunged into the forest at Wantisden and burned out. Six of the crew were killed, but the 19-year-old rear gunner, although injured, survived the crash.

The immense runway was the scene of frenzied activity on 24th March, 1945, when it was host to a large fleet of General Aircraft Hamilcar and Airspeed Horsa heavy gliders and their Handley-Page Halifax tugs. This was one of the marshalling and take-off areas for "Operation Varsity", the

Lined up on the Sutton Heath runway, General Aircraft Hamilcar and Airspeed Horsa gliders and Handley-Page Halifax tugs await take-off for "Operation Varsity", the airborne crossing of the Rhine.   *Mrs D. Pettitt*

airborne crossing of the Rhine. The aircraft employed were forty-eight Hamilcars, some of which carried Locust T.9 tanks, and twelve Horsas, both types being towed by sixty Halifax Mk. IIIs and Mk. VIIs of Nos. 298 and 644 Squadrons of No. 38 Group. For five days previously, hosts of khaki-clad men had been busily engaged in loading the gliders with the light tanks, cars, trucks and all the necessary equipment for the operation.

An operation of this magnitude of necessity takes time to execute, but at 06.00 hours on 24th March the whole of the aerial armada was airborne within thirty-six minutes. After they had flown around the surrounding airspace for some time they formed up into their battle formations and headed out over the North Sea, their destination being the Wesel area of Germany. Apart from the odd casualty over the sea, the Woodbridge armada arrived complete at the landing zone at the beginning of what was to be a successful operation.

Flight Lieutenant Peter Rowland recalls the operation as seen from the strip:

"On Thursday, 15th March, some new and interesting types appeared in the shape of two General Aircraft Hamilcars and three Airspeed Horsa heavy gliders towed in by Handley-Page Halifaxes from No. 38 Group. Early on Sunday, 18th March, more gliders and tugs arrived, and by Wednesday, the 21st, a large tented accommodation area had been established just back from the runway towards the eastern end. It reminded me of World War One pictures and we wondered what all these Army types, sporting R.A.F.-type wings, were up to. We were all sure that we did not envy them their task, whatever it was.

"From this date the entire Station was confined to camp and all mail was prevented from leaving the camp, so we knew that something big was about to take place. To increase the tension, several V1s passed over, making their curious chattering roar which thankfully faded into the distance. The new residents kept to their now very large camp, as they were all very conscious of the security and secrecy and only the R.A.F. types visited the Camp Cinema that evening for the showing of *Melody Inn*.

"Friday dawned clear and bright and turned into a glorious warm sunny spring day. During the afternoon all the gliders and tugs were marshalled in orderly lines down at the far end of the runway, the gliders ranged in three rows pointing straight down the tarmac, with a long row of Halifax tugs on either side of them facing inwards at 45 degrees. It was all done meticulously, right down to the towing hawsers laid out on the ground from each of the gliders, an impressive sight indeed spread over the vast Woodbridge runway. The strip had been closed to all other flying the previous day and was shut down until the armada had moved off.

"On Saturday, 24th March, just as the sun was rising the mass take-off commenced, the gliders being dragged laboriously into the air by the straining Halifaxes, two poor devils crashing just after getting into the air, no doubt taking all with them. We paused for a while in silent thought and commiseration at this deadly dangerous mission that the departing men had to see through — it certainly was a different war to the one which we normally experienced, as we expected to come home to base while they were being projected into an alien place and left there to fight and live or die. This operation we learned later was the airborne crossing of the Rhine and the final assault into Germany itself."

The Airspeed A.S.58 Horsa II which took part in many large airborne operations such as that launched from Sutton Heath on Saturday, 24th March, 1945.   *British Aircraft Corporation*

The end of the war was in sight and some of the R.A.F. heavy bombers were turning their attention from offensive operations to something very different, dropping food supplies to the occupied countries which were running very short of food as a result of the war. It was an operation which did have its dangers, as a Suffolk-based Lancaster, NF.995 of No. 186 Squadron from Stradishall, found in April, 1945.

Captained by Pilot Officer Rose, the Stradishall Lancaster was taking part in "Operation Manna" when it was hit by German small arms fire as it flew over the Waalhaven area near Rotterdam. The container release mechanism was damaged so that he could not "deliver his groceries" and Pilot Officer Rose decided to return to base, but when he arrived over Stradishall he found that his undercarriage was also inoperative. The usual procedure of jerking the aircraft resulted only in the groceries being distributed around the surrounding villages, so the Lancaster made for Sutton Heath and a successful wheels-up landing.

April saw the tempo lessening. Only 159 aircraft used the runway during that month, better weather enabling the homeward-bound aircraft to make their bases safely and only those suffering technical troubles or battle damage needed the safety of the long runway. One arrival, however, caused the ground crews considerable anxiety, this being a Halifax of Coastal Command which had requested emergency facilities on 9th April. Battle damage had caused the mid-upper turret to be blown off and the gunner had fallen through the shattered bomb bay, his parachute harness snagging on the twisted wreckage. He hung suspended in space, his fellow crew members having given him up for lost. The Halifax reached Sutton Heath and landed safely. Although the unfortunate gunner had been dangling beneath the aircraft for three and a half hours and his oxygen mask and goggles had scraped the concrete runway on touchdown, apart from shock and exposure he was unhurt.

With only forty-seven landings in May and twenty-four in June, the work of the Station had almost finished. The main task of the airfield staff was cleaning up and salvaging the great piles of wreckage which had accumulated. Lorry loads were carted to Melton railway station, where a constant supply of open railway trucks were loaded with the valuable metals which had originated from both sides of the Atlantic Ocean.

It would be extremely difficult to assess the worth of Woodbridge/Sutton Heath in its role as an Emergency Landing Ground and the tremendous effect that it must have had on the morale of Bomber Command crews and the war effort in general. Countless lives were saved as the strip was ideally placed to receive crippled aircraft coming in from over the North Sea, whose crews were at the point of almost total fatigue even if they were uninjured. Both the R.A.F. and U.S.A.A.F. were fully engaged in their relentless day and night offensive against the Third Reich, and it was for this very reason that Woodbridge/Sutton Heath's role was a twenty-four-hour, seven-days-a-week task. The work of the Station was continuous as wrecks had to be cleared and salvaged, empty aircraft tanks replenished, minor damage repaired and servicing carried out to enable many of the visitors eventually to return to their home bases.

It was a station that almost all Bomber Command crews knew of. Very many were extremely glad to see it for the first time and to know that it was there should they ever need it again.

CHAPTER EIGHT

Eye Witness

IT IS a great pleasure to record the personal reminiscences of officers and men who served alongside the gigantic strip, recollections that reveal the ups and downs of those hectic days.

Mr Jack Bushby, of Leek, Staffordshire, recalled his days at Woodbridge at length:

"I was there from October, 1943, to July, 1944. I had just been commissioned in the Technical Branch (Engineering) and sent to No. 54 Maintenance Unit at Cambridge, which was the Repair and Salvage Unit for Cambridgeshire, Bedfordshire, Huntingdonshire, Norfolk and Suffolk. After a few weeks crash-inspecting around the area, I was sent to Woodbridge to take charge of the No. 54 M.U. detachment there. We were responsible for clearing crashed aircraft from the runway, assisting with on-site repairs (Category AC), dismantling and salvaging parts from 'write-offs', etc. As you can imagine this was a pretty full-time job, and in addition we coped with any other crashes within the Ipswich area, in to about Sudbury and out to the coast.

"My fellow officers at the time were Flying Officers Brown and Newnham, who were with the R.A.F. Regiment Anti-Aircraft Squadron on site to protect the runway. Flying Officer Horsenell looked after the Accounts, Flight Lieutenant Hood and Flying Officer Connell were the much overworked Medical Staff, Flying Officer Garstang was the Equipment Officer, while Flying Officer Reeves was from the Petroleum Warfare Department at Bradwell Bay, Essex, and was at Woodbridge to supervise the installation of F.I.D.O. and its operation.

"Flight Lieutenant McLeod of Flying Control had undergone extensive plastic surgery after crashing a Spitfire and having his face mixed up with the instrument panel. The Station Commander was Wing Commander Burnside, one of the best I have ever met, who had been a Squadron Commander on Halifaxes and after two or three tours of operations had been given the job at Woodbridge. His Adjutant was Flight Lieutenant Boucher, and Squadron Leader Dillnutt was the Local Defence Liaison Officer, while Squadron Leader Martin, who was on rest from operations, assisted with the Flying Control duties.

"The R.A.F. Regiment was commanded by Squadron Leader Binet-Godfrey, an ex-Glamorganshire county cricketer with an excellent Welsh voice that was well exercised in the Mess. He was assisted in this command by his No. 2, Flight Lieutenant Lavis. Others were Pilot Officer Simmonds, also in Accounts, and Assistant Adjutant Flying Officer Higgs, R.A.F. Regiment, Pilot Officer Gilchrist, who had just been promoted from Warrant Officer and, resting from ops, helped out in the Control Tower. Pilot Officer Taylor had the often exacting task of Armament Officer, while Flight Lieutenant Frankland was the Station Engineering Officer.

"When I first arrived, there were only nine officers on the station and things were beginning to warm up. I remember looking with awe on the huge runway, 3,000 yards of tarmac with a further 500 yards of overshoot on the grass, 250 yards wide. It had been cut through Forestry Commission plantations and must have involved felling thousands of trees. Living and working accommodation, including the Messes, consisted of Nissen huts.

"My first morning there I was signalled from Cambridge to pick up a Heinkel which had crashed at Claydon. This turned out to be a rather tricky job because it had come down in a very muddy spot, and we eventually had to enlist the aid of a tank from a nearby R.E.M.E. Recovery Unit to drag the aircraft from the mire. Another early recollection is of a U.S.A.A.F. Martin Marauder which came in with a burst tyre and landed away over on the far

The officers of R.A.F. Woodbridge muster for a photograph in April, 1944. Back row, left to right: Flying Officer Brown, Flight Lieutenant Horsenell, Flying Officer Newnham, Flying Officer Connell, Flight Lieutenant Hood, Flying Officer Garstang, Flying Officer Reeves. Seated: Flight Lieutenant McLeod, Flight Lieutenant Boucher, Squadron Leader Dillnutt, Wing Commander Burnside, Squadron Leader Martin, Squadron Leader Binet-Godfrey, Flight Lieutenant Lavis. Front row, seated on ground: Pilot Officer Simmonds, Pilot Officer Hyde, Flying Officer Higgs, Pilot Officer Gilchrist, Pilot Officer Taylor, Pilot Officer Bushby.
Mr Jack Bushby

The aircraft which caused so much bother to Pilot Officer Jack Bushby, a Martin B-26 Marauder operating from Rougham, near Bury St Edmunds. The heavy forward armanent is in blisters on the fuselage sides.   *Mr and Mrs Hall*

side of the runway. The starboard undercarriage collapsed, causing it to slew off into the trees. I went out with my salvage crew to jack it up and then tow it across the runway to a hard standing where it could wait for an American repair party. However, it had split a belly tank and petrol was dripping out; the runway being mainly a bitumen surface laid on hardcore, it was obvious that by the time we got it across a large part of the runway surface would have been badly damaged by the leaking petrol. The aircraft's Flight Engineer and myself got into the aircraft and I asked him if there was any way we could jettison the petrol into the sand at the side of the runway where the aircraft had finished up. 'Sure,' says the engineer, and before I could stop him he 'hit' the electrical jettison switch. Of course the damn thing shorted out in the tank and up went the Marauder. I don't remember scrambling out but we both managed it, and before we could do more than get our salvage equipment out of the way the bomber was a complete write-off.

"With visions of impending doom I made my way to the Mess where the pilot, the colonel in charge of that Marauder Squadron, was having tea. 'I'm afraid we've burnt your aircraft, Sir,' I apologised. He gave me a very odd look and said 'Nev'r did like that son-of-a-bitch, Sonny. Plenty more where that came from'. And that was that, apart from some merciless leg-pulling from the rest of the R.A.F. crowd. I shudder to think what would have happened to me had it been an R.A.F. plane!

"A few nights after this all flying was off through fog (pre-F.I.D.O. days) and the nine of us, together with the Commanding Officer's charming wife, got down to some serious drinking. During the course of the evening Wing Commander Burnside got a paint-brush and some Indian Ink and with the aid of a torch, painted silhouettes of each of our heads on the Mess wall with appropriate captions. Mine I remember was 'Crasher Bushby, the man who burned the Marauder!' These paintings were still there when I left and some years later during 1964 my wife and I were around the area and called in to see the site of the old Mess. The original Nissen huts had been incorporated into the American Mess and the brick walls covered with panelling, but the Mess Sergeant told me that as far as he knew the paintings were still under the wooden panelling.

"Woodbridge, naturally enough, had its tragic side — it could be a grim place early morning of a big raid, badly shot-up aircraft, badly wounded, dead and dying crew members. We all mucked in with the clearances and never had to turn anyone away, in fact, at least one German landed by mistake and got captured for his trouble.

"One night a Lancaster with an Australian pilot landed somewhat shakily we thought and taxied in. We were aghast when we saw the aircraft, as apparently they had iced-up at about 15,000 feet over Holland and had gone into a very steep dive. It was impossible to bale out at the speed they were doing, and by super-human efforts the pilot and flight engineer had managed between them to pull it out of its dive at below two thousand feet. In the dive the dinghy had burst out from its stowage in the starboard inner engine nacelle, carried off part of the upper wing skin, hit the starboard fin and rudder, smashing the top half of these components away and completely demolishing the starboard elevator. Both ailerons had pulled away, yet the crew got it back to Woodbridge, where the pilot hoped he would get credited with 'half an op', although he had not reached the target.

"During the 1944 heavy saturation bombing of Germany it was not uncommon to have aircraft coming in with bombs stuck in them dropped from aircraft at a higher level. It must have been completely unnerving to have a 500-pounder stuck in the middle of the upper fuselage all the way back from Germany.

"Some squadrons appeared to be regular visitors. One I remember was No. 412 Squadron, Royal Canadian Air Force, based at Gransden Lodge. We had one or more of their Lancasters in each week, it seemed, and as these were Canadian built, powered with Packard-built Rolls Royce Merlin engines, they sometimes presented a little difficulty for spares. One of my most frequent visitors was their Engineering Officer on the scrounge for bits off one or the other of his Category AC (Repair on Site) aircraft we had around. This was a bit embarrassing as we wanted to keep his aircraft on the Squadron flying but on the other hand we wanted to get the repaired ones off our hands as quickly as possible. If they were to be cannibalized this would not be so easy.

"I forget 'Chuck's' name now, but he was a pilot himself and he used to come over in his Station Commander's Airspeed Oxford, not always with the C.O.'s knowledge. One nice summer's day he was over cadging and had

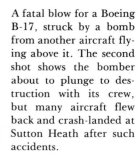

A fatal blow for a Boeing B-17, struck by a bomb from another aircraft flying above it. The second shot shows the bomber about to plunge to destruction with its crew, but many aircraft flew back and crash-landed at Sutton Heath after such accidents.

parked the Oxford on a dispersal about fifty yards from my Nissen hut. While he was trying his sales talk, a B-17 Fortress from one of the U.S.A.F. bases in Suffolk came in with two engines out of action on one side. The Fort touched down in the centre of the runway, went into a violent swing, hit and fractured the F.I.D.O. pipelines and caught fire, finishing up alongside the Oxford which, being of all wooden construction, was a pile of smouldering wood ashes before everything else was under control. The poor Canadian was right up the wall over this and I still don't know whether he returned to Gransden Lodge or deserted! Anyway it was the last time I ever saw him. I had an excellent recording of this incident as Flight Lieutenant Ella, who was a Technical Intelligence Officer with No. 54 Maintenance Unit, photographed the events, but the precious prints were lost when I was evacuated from the Iranian oilfields during 1951 and Doctor Mossadegh's henchmen omitted to send my possessions home.

"Another incident involving a Fortress, this time with a Lancaster, could have had disastrous results. It was again summer and early evening when we had a warning that a Lancaster had burst a tyre on take-off and was coming in at Woodbridge to have the wheel changed before continuing its operation. This was not uncommon, with care it was fairly routine and most pilots seemed to be able to keep the weight on the sound wheel until they slowed down, though it was very dodgy in this case with a full bomb load aboard. Anyway, the Lancaster got down nearly in one piece and we were away across the runway with the jacks and a spare wheel expecting to have the lame duck away in about twenty minutes. We had just started to jack it up when a broadcast on the Tannoy told us to clear the runway as a Fortress returning from a daylight raid was coming in badly shot-up and without radio. It was impossible to contact the Fort but despite a red flare at him he was in no condition to go round again and landed fair and square on the Lancaster, breaking its back and trapping the bombs inside.

"Everyone including the crew of the Fortress got clear, and then Eric Taylor, our Armament Officer, telephoned the Lancaster's home base for

An Airspeed Oxford similar to the one destroyed at Sutton Heath after being hit by an American bomber.

particulars of the bomb load. He was informed that the bombs had been fused before leaving base and were fully armed, with delay set for noon next day! Nothing for it but to start salvage. The Fortress had to be broken up and transported piecemeal off the Lancaster, then the Lanc parts hoisted up and separated to get the bombs out. The bombs got away eventually early next morning and the Bomb Disposal lads exploded them on the beach at Orfordness before zero hour. There were a few gallons of sweat around Woodbridge that night!

"One of our frequent types of incident was when we had a B-24 Liberator landing without brake pressure. There were quite a few 'Lib' units nearby and as this aircraft had a tricycle undercarriage with a nosewheel it required even more than Woodbridge's length of runway to stop without brakes. I remember one pilot telling me that they had tried out a Liberator at Muroc Dry Lake, now Edwards Air Force Base, in California, which is situated on a vast dried-up lake bed, and the Liberator had taken four miles to roll to a stop! Incidentally this is the same site that was used for the landing ground for the Space Shuttle flights.

"The pilots evolved a technique of sending all thirteen or so of the crew into the tail to hold it on to the ground to slow up and it used to be a fantastic pyrotechnic display of sparks as the fuselage skin rubbed away on the runway. Later the lower fuselage was modified to incorporate a skid to cover this emergency.

"A couple of days before D-Day my salvage crew from Woodbridge collected a Miles Martinet target tug aircraft based at Ipswich Airport which had crashed on Felixstowe Golf Links. The military traffic was so dense that we put it on the Queen Mary* for the base and then left the lads with the wreck to come back in the morning while I went on to Woodbridge. However that night came the security clamp-down on the embarkation areas for the great day and my crew were locked in until the invasion was actually announced later that day.

"For half the time I was at Woodbridge I lived out of camp with my wife at Clopton, where we stayed with the Vicar and his wife. One character I remember at Woodbridge was the first Flying Control Officer, Squadron Leader Whitting. A couple of nights after I arrived we had a party and everyone put on their best blue and Squadron Leader Whitting, who was around forty, was wearing a medal ribbon (a single one) that I did not recognize. I asked the Commanding Officer if he could enlighten me, to find that he didn't know either. He called the Adjutant who said, 'Oh yes, his records have just arrived and it's the George Medal'. Remember this was 1943, and most of us hadn't seen a George Medal. Apparently, Whitting was quite a character, a classical scholar and bachelor who lived in Chelsea between walking tours around Greece and the Balkans. During the 1940 Blitz, before he joined up, he had formed himself into what amounted to a one man bomb disposal squad. He got well reprimanded by the authorities and the George Medal!"

Squadron Leader Bill Williams, of No. 9 Squadron, recalls:

"My squadron had been diverted after an abortive trip to Paderborn in Germany carrying the twelve thousand pound Tallboy bomb. On landing one of the Lancasters picked up a piece of metal in one of its tyres, which quickly became deeply embedded. This of course necessitated a wheel change, so the Armament Team for Bardney, our home base, was sent for to do the necessary removal of the bomb.

"The aircraft was standing on grass and the bomb doors were opened, which was more than likely the first time most of the large ground crew standing around had seen a Tallboy. The lads of No. 9 Squadron Bomb Team, incidently a jolly good crowd of chaps, started to lower the bomb, then they thought that they would have a little fun and let the bomb run and crash

*R.A.F. lorry for carrying aircraft.

down on to the ground. You can imagine the panic that ensued as the whole crowd of onlookers suddenly wanted to be somewhere else. The fact that the bomb had been rendered safe before the start of the operation made little difference! I don't think there were any cases of heart failure, but there were probably several near misses!"

Another Woodbridge resident of long standing, Flight Lieutenant Peter Rowland, remembered his days on the strip:

"On 1st January, 1945, at 7.30 in the evening when on indefinite leave since the middle of December, and enjoying the protracted rest and idleness after the completion of my operational tour as a Flight Engineer with No. 149 Squadron in No. 3 Group, Bomber Command, I received a telegram recalling me to the Squadron. The next morning found me on the train on the way back to Norfolk and wondering what my future fates were to be during the forthcoming stand-down from operations.

"I was happy to learn that I had a posting to Woodbridge, the Emergency Landing Ground every aircrew member appreciated but hoped that he would never have the opportunity to visit. My job was to be the interrogation of British aircrew of aircraft serviceability and damage sustained and to complete records for same. It promised to be an interesting and active task with some responsibility and was not too far from home. I was well pleased with the news, as after all it was still very closely connected with flying and aircraft, which were the great interest of my life, and Woodbridge promised plenty of activity and excitement. After lunch next day, Flying Officer Dedman gave me a lift with my kit in the Oxford over to Woodbridge and it was goodbye to Methwold and squadron days.

"My new home, I noted on that first evening, seemed to be a very lovely place, quite isolated and carved out of the pine forests—there was not even a

The men of R.A.F. Woodbridge muster in front of the control tower during one of their less busy moments. *Mr Cheetham*

W.A.A.F. Section there. Many flying bombs passed over our heads that night and quite a few were shot down that we could hear.

"After briefing in the morning as to my duties, I settled down to draft out a form on which to compile the information that was required, with details of aircraft landing, serviceability reports, etc. I was able to draw a Station bicycle, Serial Number WE.560 just like an aircraft, to get about on duty—jolly handy. Incidentally the serial number of my bicycle was later used on an Auster Mark T7.

"Another Flight Engineer, Ralph, had arrived on a similar posting so together we could work round the clock on alternate 24-hour shifts. After being on all night there would be that dreary but thankful trek back in the cold and often gloomy dawn to an equally cold, damp room and bed.

"My first bit of excitement was not long in coming, as on the very next morning, 5th January, I was cycling along the dispersal loop, indulging in a spot of exploration of the station environment. Unseen above the low 10/10 cloud it sounded as if the whole American Eighth Air Force was up in strength, buzzing about noisily. Suddenly amid the uproar came a weird and alarming screaming sound, quite near and above, and then just in front of me, literally dropping straight out of the cloud, appeared a P-47 Thunderbolt. It came plummeting down, gyrating round and round quite slowly in a flat spin, a heart-stopping moment. It was just like 'Tailspin Tommy' in those Saturday morning pictures, I thought at that moment.

"Horrified, I realised that it was not going to pull out, as the great fat fighter fell out of the sky, still turning relentlessly round and round in a level and flat altitude. Then the canopy came away and the pilot leaped out, his parachute partially opening straight away. He swung violently about twice before hitting the curved roof of a Nissen hut, and ended his short descent with an undignified slither down to the ground, completely winded, a mere few seconds after his aircraft had smashed down plumb across the dispersal loop with a tremendous thud, and not so very far in front of where I stood rooted to the spot.

"For an instant, which in that arrested moment seemed an eternity, it sat there seemingly quite whole and solid before exploding into a roaring inferno, disappearing for ever in a huge welter of fire, a great plume of blood-red and oily smoke accompanied by the fierce crackle and whizz of exploding ammunition in nightmarish orchestration. Later we heard that the pilot was O.K. and were all relieved at the good news.

"In the afternoon of the same day we were treated to the spectacle of a damaged B-17 Fortress making a landing on only one wheel while we all held our breath and crossed our fingers. The pilot made a grand job of it, bringing her in as gently and sedately as one could imagine and setting the big heavy plane down very softly on the one wheel. He managed to hold it up level for a

A Republic P-47D, serial 28559 of the 356th Fighter Group, which came to grief in the woods and bears all the hallmarks of a write-off. *U.S.A.F./Mactaggart*

surprising distance, chased by a posse of fire and crash tenders, until it finally toppled over on to its port wing at quite a slow speed and slewed round, now out of control, with the airscrews bending crazily as they slapped into the concrete. Then all was still!

"Within seconds, 'bods' appeared from all parts of the bomber and scampered off a few paces in all directions, then stopped and looked back a trifle self-consciously as nothing more happened and the dormant hulk disappeared under a blanket of white foam swiftly laid down by the crash tenders.

"My first weekend at Woodbridge saw me on duty Saturday and Sunday. It was very cold and frosty, with snow falls. The dodgy weather prevented flying and we had no visitors during the daylight hours of Saturday, but I had to stand-to for landings from 17.30 until 01.00 and then slept round until eleven o'clock on Sunday. I then worked the standby interrogation from 19.00 hours until 04.00 next day. Only one Lancaster and a Mosquito came in, so I went to the Camp Cinema to see *Double Indemnity*.

"Saturday, 13th January, was a busy day for Woodbridge, for we recorded a massive diversion of 106 B-17s of the U.S.A.A.F. I'd not seen so many aircraft all together—they went on coming in endlessly and trundled past us spectators to park, stacked tightly together. What a sight to us of the R.A.F., used only to the dull black and camouflage. All these silver planes, gleaming so brightly with the dazzling profusion of multi-coloured stripes, bands and flashes, all manner of gaudy painted motifs, insignia, emblems,

151

names and pin-ups. The air was filled with that lovely distinctive breathy, wheezing rumble of hundreds of Wright Cyclone radial engines, and there were all those guns sticking out from everywhere. In not much more than half an hour the Station had its complement increased by over a thousand aircrew!

"During the following night we had thirty-nine R.A.F. aircraft came in, but for Monday I recorded that it had been a quiet duty, only three aircraft made emergency landings.

"I now found that I had been nominated Entertainments Officer, a job for which I was totally unqualified and which I did not relish much. I was not at all confident. However, things had been very quiet owing to the very bad weather for three days, so a camp dance was organised at short notice for Saturday night. Local 'female talent' was press-ganged and transport laid on to supplement the few wives and sweethearts available. I ran the bar and took £8 8s 9d. (£8.44) over the counter, a major success! It was also recorded in my diary that I bought my cigarette and sweet ration—twenty Craven "A", thirty Players, two fives of Player's Weights, a Mars bar, a bar of chocolate and an orange—all for 5s. 7½d. (28p).

"Towards the end of the week the weather became awful, with heavy frost and tons of snow, so on Saturday night a party of us from the Officers' Mess went to a dance in Ipswich. Pilot Officer Young provided the car, which was well loaded with Squadron Leader Payne, Squadron Leader Carter, Flight Lieutenant Boucher and myself. It was 4.30 a.m. before we got back, after a hairy time ploughing our way through the snow, but we all made it to the Mess for breakfast. There were several landings that Sunday night, some from Berlin, and quite a busy night was spent looking after all the arrivals.

"The Dance Band of Bomber Command came to entertain us on Monday afternoon and gave a super concert, *Bugle Call Rag* and all the contemporary jazz, great stuff. It was the first time that most of us realised that such an outfit of our own existed, and we felt quite honoured to be so privileged. The evening shift was exciting, with twenty-seven Mosquitoes to deal with, and then I was Orderly Officer, inspecting the guard and pickets, seeing those who might be on charges detained in custody, doing the rounds including the Airmen's Mess, and, of course, running the flag down.

"To amuse myself during the empty days I drew a .38 pistol from the Armoury and put in a bit of practice on the range. I was beginning to feel something akin to a cavalryman without a horse!

"Tuesday, 13th February, was a very busy night with eighteen aircraft coming in, all the crews to be interrogated and serviceability and damage reports to be made up. We also found out that day that my colleague Ralph had been appointed Station Motor Transport Officer, which meant that I would have to do all the engineering interrogation on my own, except when released on a 36-hour pass. A telephone was rigged up in my billet so that

Flying Control could summon me to the Interrogation Room when aircraft were in the circuit at night, as I was now on call every night. So now in the middle of some dark, cold or freezing night one could catch a glimpse of a somewhat bedraggled figure cycling through the woods to the action, half asleep and cursing his misfortune, and with trousers, tunic, greatcoat and muffler hastily cast on over pyjamas.

"Next day came the all-important news that I was to be made up to Flying Officer and a whole lot more cash, of course.

"I had a very interesting day the next week when the Officer in Charge of the Salvage Team with No. 54 Maintenance Unit invited me along with them to recover a Lancaster which had been ditched in the River Orwell, the expedition to take place on 22nd February, 1945. The job was something unusual for them as the aircraft had been 'ditched' and was to be recovered from the water in a very isolated spot. Fields, woods and farmland had to be negotiated to reach the scene, a bit of an adventure in itself for our convoy of lorries, tractors and the Coles crane. The operation was timed for low tide, of course, and the poor old 'Lanc' looked a very sorry sight, laying half submerged

Not all crippled aircraft made it to the Emergency Landing Ground. This Boeing B-17F, serial 230157 of the 91st Bomb Group based at Bassingbourn, which appears to have lost its port inner motor, crashed in open country. *U.S.A.F.*

in the mud. Eventually, after a great deal of struggling, cables were passed around her and she was dragged gradually to the bank of the river, where she was left to be broken up another day.

"During the week we learned that a member of the Women's Land Army had been killed in the nearby forest when a long-range drop tank had fallen from an American fighter. There was a notice in the local newspaper that week announcing that Miss Queenie Wells, one of two Forestry girls, of Eley Hill, Capel St Andrew, working in an isolated spot, had been killed when the pilot of an 8th Air Force North American Mustang jettisoned his auxiliary petrol tank after the aircraft had suffered an engine fire after take-off. He landed safely.

"On Saturday, 3rd March, Luftwaffe intruders shot up aircraft in the Woodbridge circuit and a B-17 Fortress came in damaged by one of them, as

Douglas C-47, a maid-of-all-work known in the R.A.F. as the Dakota.   *U.S.A.F.*

well as a B-24 Liberator, a Hawker Tempest fighter and two de Havilland Mosquitoes, all in one sort of trouble or another. There was further intruder activity the following night and we were informed of a Douglas Dakota being shot down near the coast, probably by our own anti-aircraft fire.

"Tuesday, 7th March, I got airborne in Avro Anson NK.711, flown by Flying Officer Wright from No. 6 Group, quite a red letter day for me as it was the first time that I had managed to get my feet off the ground in three months. The aircraft was a bit of a boneshaker and it took quite a time to get the wheels cranked-up, by hand, all very prehistoric. (The task of getting the wheels up in an Anson was always the privilege of the passenger sitting next to the pilot—the initiated always sat down at the other end of the fuselage!) We took fifty minutes to reach Hartford Bridge in Surrey, and then a ten-minute hop just over the county boundary to Odiham in Hampshire for some reason or other, but the great thing was that I got in three take-offs and landings, which helped to pass a very enjoyable day.

"As we had a party of Air Training Corps cadets and Army personnel on the Station at the time, Pilot Officer Young of the Bomb Ballistic Unit was detailed to take up parties of them in the Lancaster Mark VI which he flew for that unit. He asked me to fly as Flight Engineer with him as his own crewman was on a weekend pass. For some time I had cast envious eyes on the beautiful 'Lanc' which flew regularly on bombing trials and as I had watched it trundle off and into the blue I had longed to be on the flight deck. Now, three and a half months since staggering back from Cologne badly shot up by flak and with one of our crew dead, I was to get my hands on a Lancaster again, especially this special Mark VI with its extra-powerful engines.

"We flew three trips, each of forty minutes, under the category of local flying, the first two with A.T.C. cadets and the third one with the Army types. As a diversion, the pilot decided to try out some feathering procedures with the airscrews, so we shut down one outer engine and feathered the airscrew, and then to raise the blood pressure of the 'brown types' the outer engine on the other side was shut down as well and the 'prop' feathered. With two airscrews majestically and dramatically still and lifeless, we sailed along in grand style; it was great fun to point out these features to our passengers and to see their apprehensive and worried expressions. To show there was no ill feeling Pilot Officer Young then decided to bring the bomber in on two engines only, which he did with great dexterity.

"As we were really 'out in the sticks' the nearest large centre of population was Ipswich, which we made for as time and finances allowed. I recall meeting a young lady and going to the cinema and then finally along to a dance at the Ipswich Borough General Hospital on the east side of the town. Transport being what it was, we walked the five miles back to Woodbridge before we were collected for the remainder of the journey.

"I was on standby duty on 15th March when at 19.30 hours a B-17 Fortress approached the strip in terrible trouble, radioing Maydays and requesting a 'straight-in pancake' with full emergency standby. It had been severely damaged, with half the fuselage torn away by an anti-aircraft shell which had exploded amidships, aft of the mainplane. I did not like to think of the fate of the waist gunners. It was an awesome sight to behold and I wondered in amazement and respect at this Boeing — how in hell was the thing holding together to get back this far? Nevertheless, she gently motored in towards a blanket of foam which had been quickly put down. The pilot set her down nice and tenderly, wheels down, while a posse of crash tenders, fire engines and ambulances made frantic pursuit either side of her.

"Our equipment at Woodbridge was very advanced, a great deal of it being provided by the U.S.A.F. It included vehicles with remotely controlled foam sprayers on long telescopic arms for getting right into a blazing wreck. This was all very different from standard Squadron equipment.

"Getting back to earth was a bit too much for the damaged Fort, as under her own weight she broke clean in half, with the bottom of the broken fuselage dropping down on to the concrete and the back of the mainplanes scraping along, showering sparks. The airscrews bent and deflected grotesquely as they jerked to a standstill, stalling the motors with a screeching, grinding sound that was ghastly to hear. The tail end of the bomber slewed round and spun to a standstill, then all was suddenly still and quiet after the bedlam. Within seconds everything was completely buried under thick white foam — I thought the crew would be suffocated. There was no fire, a tribute to the crash and fire crews. The crew were all retrieved safe and sound and rushed away in ambulances to hospital after their terrible ordeal. The aircraft's identification markings were a letter L within a triangle on the fin, which we now know belonged to the 381st Bomb Group operating from Ridgewell, Essex, and its individual aircraft letter was J.

"After a week of pleasant weather, Monday 26th March was lousy, overcast, dull and raining and we had a very nasty Mustang crash. With a wild screeching howl, this aircraft hurtled out of the murk with startling suddenness to explode with a sickening thud into the pine trees just beyond the far side of the runway, the place being marked by the familiar ball of dirty, oily smoke rising up horrifically into the sky.

"A group of us went across a little after the crash and watched the fire crews. The area about the point of impact was a scene of utter devastation, with trees blasted down to smouldering stumps stripped of branches and foliage. A thick pungent smell of scorching and burnt oil was overwhelming and caught in your throat. The remains of the Mustang lay covered in deep foam in a crater of a size which surprised me, it must have been all of ten to twelve feet deep. From pieces flung clear it had been established that it was indeed a P-51 Mustang from the U.S. 8th Air Force. One of the chaps told us that the pilot had been found, looking at first glance to be sitting quite normally on the ground against a tree, but very dead, poor fellow. It was a shocking and saddening scene of utter sudden disaster.

A de Havilland D.H.98 Mosquito, one of a type which often landed at Sutton Heath short of fuel after long-range missions over Occupied Europe. *de Havilland*

"Next day we had one Mosquito and a Lancaster in and more flying bombs, which were all shot down by the Ack-Ack boys. During the morning I was fortunate enough to be able to draw a petrol ration of eight gallons in readiness for official leave, to which I had been greatly looking forward.

"Back on the Unit on 8th April, I had a 'Mossie'* in at 02.00 hours, but the rest of the week was quiet. Some of us went to a local 'hop' in Woodbridge one evening and a Liberty Run was organised to Ipswich for Saturday night. Later that night we had a Liberator, a Fortress and three Mosquitoes in for safe landings. Another 'Mossie' arrived at 02.00 hours on Monday morning, obviously a popular time for these chaps! Two more arrived during the week, both at 02.00 hours. The highlight of Monday evening was the arrival of the E.N.S.A.† concert party which came to put on a show for us.

"During the next three weeks of April we found that we were only getting the odd Mosquito in at night, as these chaps were operating on lone high-altitude sorties, often to Berlin, to lob in their individual loads, so keeping up a nightly attack and giving the citizens of that city very little respite. Some of the 'Mossies' carried a 4,000 lb 'cookie' (R.A.F. slang for the 4,000 lb bomb), the load of a B-17 in a twin-engined, wooden aeroplane, at twice the speed and with only two crew, and not a single gun between them!

"A lot of the arrivals had suffered an engine failure of one sort or another, with the poor old Merlin, now highly stressed and over-boosted, blowing up on them with resultant loss of services such as hydraulics, brakes and electrics. There were often cases of connecting rods sticking out of crankcases!

"A dear old Stirling was a rare visitor during the night of 26th April, and this was followed by a couple of 'Mossies'.

"In those last few weeks before the war in Europe was suddenly to end, at midnight on 7th May, we were having quite a brisk social round of dances in the vicinity, for the pace of war was slackening for us at Woodbridge. The W.A.A.F.s at their radar station at nearby Bawdsey Manor invited us over to the dances on three occasions and these were very popular indeed. We also went to Melton, to the R.A.F. Mustang base at Bentwaters, and to the Ipswich Borough General Hospital with its charming nurses.

"During May I had the chance of a trip in the Oxford LX.242, flown by Squadron Leader Payne, who was engaged on some errand or other, and I was able to enter another fifty minutes in my now greatly neglected log book.

"On Tuesday, 8th May, it was Victory in Europe Day (V.E. Day) and we all went into Woodbridge to join in the joyous celebrations. Everybody was out in the streets, lots of drinking and dancing, and wondering in awe and amazement at all the lights glaring out, with doors open and blackouts undrawn. It was all so sudden after those years of darkness. And, perhaps best

*Mosquito.
†Entertainment National Service Association.

of all, lots of girls to hug and kiss. It was indeed a wondrous, almost unreal night.

"The following night I pranged my car into the back of one of those tall Army trucks as I stopped at the fish and chip shop on the Woodbridge road. I simply did not see it or notice its tiny rear lights in the darkness just beyond the brilliant glare of light which streamed out from the now naked window across the road. The impact pushed the radiator back into the fan and away went the water in a great cloud of steam. The chips didn't taste so good either! I phoned the station to be rescued and it took hours for someone to get organized with a pick-up to bring us in.

"At the weekend we had a Lancaster in with undercarriage trouble which was landed successfully. It was carrying twenty-four ex-P.O.W.s, and we felt sorry for them returning home to get caught up with a dodgy emergency like that, after all that they had been through, but it turned out all right in the end. By that time I don't suppose they cared less where they landed as long as it was in the U.K.

"In the evening the unit put on a grand V.E. Dance at Woodbridge Grammar School. It was a super affair. We had laid on coaches and trucks to bring in the girls from all over the place, and the event certainly did the R.A.F. justice. It had been a very hot day and it was a novelty having doors and windows wide open and no curtains drawn and the freedom to wander in and out with lights all over the place, instead of all that creeping about in the dark.

"Another 'Lanc' came in on Monday, having aborted from another P.O.W. mission, otherwise things were quiet except for our off-duty activities. From now on, although the station still stood-by fully manned for any emergency, there was little to do and I seem to have had a 36 or 48-hour pass every two to three weeks, plus days off here and there.

"For members of aircrew who had completed a tour of operations around last November, like me, the time would be approaching for a posting back to a squadron. During my last leave I had received a letter from No. 3 Group advising me of a pending posting to South East Asia Command. Now, I did not fancy my luck in the Far East theatre of operations at all, what with all those Japs and all that water to fly over, but it was No. 5 Group who were standing by for that trip, I think, so I was feeling that I was sitting fairly safe.

"My last chance of getting airborne at Woodbridge came on 6th July when I was allocated a place on the Lancaster WP-R 'Roger' which was flown over from No. 90 Squadron at Tuddenham for a 'Baedecker' trip to view the bombing damage in Germany. It was a very great disappointment when the skipper had to abort the trip after getting as far as Aachen, right on the German border, because the weather was too bad for us with 10/10 cloud low down. It was my first and last opportunity to see the 'other side' where so many

An engine which became detached from a P-47 Thunderbolt as a result of a crash landing. Evidence of the impact is seen in the airscrew blades, wrapped around the cylinders.

U.S.A.F./Mactaggart

of us had flown to fight our war for so many years. Thus ended the last flight I was ever to have in the Lancaster, or indeed in an R.A.F. aircraft, except for a joyride in a Harvard in Cyprus and a transit in Egypt in an Anson.

"A week later I was posted from Woodbridge and found myself at Catterick, to be made redundant from aircrew and transferred into the Equipment Branch."

An ex-member of No. 54 Maintenance Unit, Mr Bert Twiddy, of Ipswich, remembers his days on Sutton Heath:

"Our parent unit was based at Newmarket Heath, and Sutton Heath was a detachment which supplied the majority of the personnel connected with the removal and salvage of the Sutton Heath crashes. Work was carried out on a shift system so that adequate staff and equipment were always available to

159

cover any emergencies. Aircraft of all types and sizes turned up in all states of disrepair, and in many cases the only equipment necessary was the ambulance. During one period the most frequent customers were the large four-engined Short Stirling bombers, which usually arrived with undercarriage troubles, and in many cases their mode of touchdown was a long slide to a standstill — more like a Sunderland flying boat. If at all possible this type of casualty was directed to the grass-surfaced overshoot section at the end of the runway in order to keep the initial facility clear, and also to lessen the risk of fire.

"One incident I well remember was the tragic crash of an Avro York four-engined transport, a brother of the Lancaster — in fact it used the same wing, engines, undercarriage and tailplane units but with a new fuselage for the transport role. The aircraft, which had been engaged on local flying, having been based on the strip for several days, touched down in the normal manner and rolled along the runway gradually losing speed. Suddenly it ground-looped and swung off the runway, crashing into the trees alongside the strip. Several fatal casualties ensued. I had the task of inhibiting the four Rolls-Royce Merlin engines so that rust and damp would not damage them before they could be removed from the wrecked aircraft.

"Many of us were local lads and 'living out' — Sleeping Out Passes were the order of the day and all manner of transport was employed for travelling to and from the Station. In my case it was as passenger in the sidecar of a motor-cycle combination owned by another Ipswich airman. For a time I also travelled with one of the officers who, seeing the state of my working uniform, sent for the Station Warrant Officer and told him to issue me with a new set of uniforms, as I travelled with him and it lowered his prestige!

"An important task to be performed when going on duty early in the morning was to go round and inspect all the rabbit snares which had been set the previous evening. This often resulted in a very useful harvest which provided us with food and whose sale brought additional money for the 'refreshment account'.

"Among the other personnel on the airfield were civilians of the Ministry of Aircraft Production (M.A.P.) who were conducting various experiments on both aircraft and equipment.

"One of the last activities just after V.E. Day involved the trips arranged by Bomber Command to enable ground crews to see the destruction that had been wrought on German targets. As a result several parties of ground staff were flown in the Lancaster to Cologne and other places which had become almost household names, and the passengers were able to see what their efforts on the ground had enabled their colleagues in the air to achieve. Several aircraft arrived in the weeks after the Armistice, but these were mainly R.A.F. bombers which were being used to fly men home from the Continent on their way to the demobilization centres and civvy street."

CHAPTER NINE

Bombs and Blind Flying

IN THE midst of war a special unit, eventually to be named the Bomb Ballistic Unit (B.B.U.), was formed at Sutton Heath to carry out air drop experiments and research into the behaviour of large aircraft-carried missiles. The long runway was ideal for getting heavily loaded and sometimes grossly overloaded aircraft off the ground, and the dropping zone at Orfordness was only a stone's throw away.

In spite of the proximity of the Orfordness dropping zone, flights were not always of short duration as a considerable amount of time was spent in getting the aircraft to the necessary altitude for the drop. The unit employed current heavy bombers of the type in regular service with the R.A.F., but they were not by any means the best examples of their types. In many cases they were rejects from operational squadrons, rogue aircraft that nobody else wanted; in other cases they were prototypes, the only aircraft of a particular variant produced.

All caused very many servicing problems for the unit's Engineering Officer. This was particularly so in the case of the prototypes as they had been almost hand-built in the first instance and any spares required had to be procured from the aircraft's makers, which often resulted in long delays while they were manufactured. It might also be added that the manufacturers would have almost finished with the aircraft, as the fact that it had not gone into production rang the death knell on its development; and the R.A.F., having bought it, were now using a more-or-less useless aircraft to the best advantage in order to recoup some of the money that had been spent on it.

Mr Youell, of Mitcham, Surrey, served on the B.B.U. from September, 1943, until April, 1945, and has many memories of events connected with this unit:

"Its job was to collate information about new-type bombs and to conduct research into trajectory, terminal velocity, etc. We flew two Lancasters, a Mosquito and a Halifax Mark IV for high-flying jobs.

"There were about forty officers and men, and for a long time we lived in tents adjacent to the runway. I remember occupying a bed, four to a bell tent, where my feet had to be covered with a gas cape to keep the snow and ice off during the first winter. We worked from a large tent which also served as Orderly Room, Workshop and Stores; in fact, there was no other accommodation until we set to and built our own out of pine logs and four-gallon petrol cans with the tops and bottoms cut off and filled with sand and earth.

"The airfield was no more than a large slab of concrete carved through a pine forest and it contained the bare essentials for operation, flying control, a fuel dump, a fairly large and busy mess hall and of course, later on, F.I.D.O. One side of the strip was bordered by trees while the other had loops curving away from it. These loops were the dispersals and working areas. Beyond B.B.U.'s loop was a vast area of crashed aircraft

Men of the Bomb Ballistics Unit outside their bell tent at Sutton Heath. Tents were used for accommodation until the first buildings were erected.

and wreckage, mostly American B-17s, B-24s, P-47s and P-51s, as well as R.A.F. Stirlings, Halifaxes and Lancasters. The only difference was the condition of the aircraft. The British types were little better than scrap, whereas the American were in most cases, to us at least, repairable. I've seen U.S.A.A.F. aircraft land and the undercarriage collapse, whereupon the machine would be picked up by cranes and stacked up on top of others on the dump.

"The arrivals would often run off the runway, and 539 were damaged in such a fashion, but in the case of the R.A.F. aircraft they were repaired and flown out again. There were times when over a hundred U.S.A.A.F. planes would be diverted to Woodbridge. I have recorded 118 in one day, many of them in terrible trouble, engines missing, tail fins shot off and very large holes through mainplanes and fuselages. Smoke and oil poured from them, some just getting down over the undershoot. One would see a great cloud of dust and sand rise up, and we would pray that it wouldn't turn to the all-too-familiar oily black smoke.

"I will always remember seeing a B-17 with the tail fin shot off which tried to make a cross-wind landing, but each time had to go round again. As he flew over, one could see right through the aircraft where the mainplane joined the fuselage, and also visible were cables and pipes trailing back in the slipstream. On the third attempt he got it right and touched down well down the runway. He had no brakes, hence no steering, and ran off the runway, smashing down Tannoy posts, ripping up F.I.D.O. pipelines and eventually coming to rest in the B.B.U. loop. We rushed over to him and opened the fuselage hatch, and then reeled back, feeling sick as the blood from the dead airmen ran from the aircraft. The pilot was the only member of the crew alive on that Fortress.

"I shall always remember my friends of the B.B.U. as we lived in our tents, and the home-made radio sets working off batteries from broken aircraft; the freezing winds and deep snow, but also the warmth of summer, the glow-worms on the Heath and the Americans shooting rabbits with automatic rifles. Bright among my recollections is the children's party when the ice-cream mixture remained cruelly soft, but a genius in our midst suggested that it be transferred to a clean dustbin and then tied into the bomb bay of our resident Lancaster, which took off and climbed several thousand feet above the strip. The hardened air-frozen children's delight was quickly returned to terra firma, to the great delight and enjoyment of the youngsters. We also made wooden toys for them, one favourite being a model Jeep which utilized control wire pulleys for wheels."

After V.E. Day the administration and servicing staff moved to more comfortable quarters at Martlesham Heath but the massive runway was still used for loaded take-offs. Other aircraft which joined the unit included several Avro Lincolns, the big brother of the Lancaster, and in due course a rare bird came on to the strength. This was a unique Lincoln, RA.716, powered by two Rolls-Royce Merlins in the inboard positions and two Rolls-Royce Avon turbo-jets in the outer engine positions. Able to climb like the proverbial "bat out of Hell", this aircraft had load capabilities which with its rapid climb made it ideal for the tasks it had to perform.

Later other odd types joined the motley collection of flying test-beds. One such addition was one of the only two examples built of the Short Sperrin, powered by four Rolls-Royce Avon jets positioned in pairs, one above the other on the mainplane. Short Brothers of Belfast had tendered for and obtained a contract to build two of these aircraft to the Specification B.14/16, although from the outset it appeared that they were to be back-up designs in case the

Vickers Valiant, Handley-Page Victor and Avro Vulcan, all then at the advanced design stage, failed to make the grade or fell behind in production. A large aircraft with a wing span of 109 feet (33.2 m) and a length of 102.3 feet (31.2 m), the Sperrin had an all-up weight of 115,000 lbs (52,000 kg) and a maximum speed of 564 m.p.h. Of great surprise to the Woodbridge servicing crews when the Sperrin first arrived was its fuel requirement of 6,170 gallons at a filling. Serialled VX.161, it arrived at Woodbridge during April, 1953, to carry out dropping trials with concrete dummies of a new generation of air-to-ground weapons which included a hush-hush item coded "Blue Danube". For this task several structural modifications had to be carried out. The Sperrin did a great deal of research using the giant runway and it was a familiar sight and sound in the district.

Another post-war arrival was a hybrid aircraft, the Avro Ashton WB.492 which had been derived from the unfortunate Avro Tudor four-engined airliner. The Tudors had been withdrawn from service with British South American Airways, headed by D. C. T. "Pathfinder" Bennett, after some of them had disappeared without trace in mysterious circumstances in the Caribbean area. In the case of the Ashton the Rolls-Royce Merlin piston engines had been replaced by four Rolls-Royce Avon turbojets, mounted side by side in pods under the mainplane. This aircraft provided very valuable service as a research and fast communication aircraft, in the latter role travelling between Martlesham Heath and Farnborough.

Because of the facility of its enormous runway and its secluded position, Woodbridge was chosen as the testing ground for the unorthodox de Havilland 108 Swallow delta-wing research jet, early flight trials of TG.283 being conducted from the site. Many serving at the strip at that time remember Flying Officer Geoffrey de Havilland, O.B.E., R.A.F.O., one of the designer's sons, who did the flying for these trials. Unfortunately this small advanced monoplane crashed on Friday, 27th September, 1946, when making a high-speed run over the Thames Estuary, and its brave pilot died in the cause of aviation research. In the two weeks preceding the crash a series of high-speed trials had been carried out with the extra power of a specially boosted de Havilland Goblin jet engine during which the absolute airspeed record in level flight was exceeded on a number of occasions. As the speeds had not been officially recorded they did not constitute new records, however.

During September, 1945, the B.B.U. was joined by another unit which housed its administration and servicing facilities at Martlesham Heath and used Woodbridge for its flying activities. This was the Blind Landing Experimental Unit, B.L.E.U. for short, which remained operational in the area until May, 1957, when it moved to the Royal Aircraft Establishment at Bedford. The two units worked side by side and shared a common site, but they differed in that one was staffed by R.A.F. personnel while the other had

The de Havilland D.H.108 Swallow research aircraft which made some of its early flights from the Sutton Heath runway. Its pilot, Geoffrey de Havilland, was killed when it crashed into the Thames Estuary in 1946.   *de Havilland*

civilian R.A.E. staff. They co-operated in all matters as a team and proved that it was possible for military and civilian personnel to work alongside each other very successfully. The aircraft servicing side of B.L.E.U. came under the control of Maintenance Command and was overall directed by the Ministry of Supply.

Becoming operational during July, 1946, the unit existed basically to provide aircraft facilities and aircrew for airborne work initiated by the Royal Aircraft Establishment. In May, 1950, B.L.E.U. merged with the Bomb Ballistic Unit to become the Armament and Instrument Experimental Unit (A.I.E.U.), the flying side of the B.L.E.U. now being known as the A.I.E.U. Instrument Flight. Day to day work consisted mainly of ballistic measurement, the unit co-operating closely with ground instrument crews at Orfordness. Piloting of the aircraft had of necessity to be of very high standard in order to place the aircraft in the desired position at the correct speed and height in order that the experiment should be a success.

Many of the "Grand Slam" ten-ton bombs were dropped off Orfordness, suitably ballasted to weight specification, to establish their flight character-istics. The North Sea also received several of the unusual "Dam Buster"

The Avro Lincoln, big brother of the Lancaster, took part in the experimental work of the Bomb Ballistics Unit, flying from both Sutton Heath and Martlesham Heath.

Hawker-Siddeley Aviation

reel-type bombs designed by Dr Barnes Wallis, these being dropped from specially modified Lancasters. Rocket trials were also conducted, the aircraft used for these flight trials being a Gloster Meteor F.9 twin-jet single-seat fighter; when flight observation records were required a two-seat de Havilland Mosquito carried out the task.

During 1952 there came another parting of the ways when the Instrument Flight was divided into two sections, the All-Weather Flight and the Rapid Landing Flight. The former was responsible for the development of an automatic approach and landing system and worked of necessity in minimal visibility conditions. Before the formation of the All-Weather Flight, the B.L.E.U. had performed several hundred automatic landings at both Woodbridge and Martlesham Heath, although the equipment used was of a highly experimental nature. The assorted collection of aircraft used for this work included a Vickers Varsity, English Electric Canberra, Douglas Dakota, Armstrong-Whitworth Albemarle, Gloster Meteor NF.11 and an Avro 707A, VX 748, the latter being a one-third scale flying evaluation model of the forthcoming Avro Vulcan bomber.

During the foggy winter days of 1951-52 and 1952-53 a de Havilland

Devon twin-engined feeder airliner which had joined the Flight carried out fog landing procedures on the Woodbridge runway and later at London Airport, where it was able to make successful landings with visibility down to 35-40 yards. During 1953 the work was transferred to an English Electric Canberra, WE.189, but this aircraft unfortunately crashed when approaching Martlesham Heath. Dropping upside down, it miraculously fell in an open paddock between a cafe and a garage at Crown Point, Martlesham, alongside the main A.12 road. Its pilot, Flight Lieutenant Coe, and his civilian Flight Observer, Mr J. Birkles, were both killed. This was the only fatality during the whole of the blind landing experimental work, which says a lot for the way that the scientists had set up the experiments, taking all safety factors into full consideration.

From this early work, beset with trials and tribulations, there stemmed the proven system of fully automatic blind approach and landing currently successfully employed by British Airways and other major airlines. This was in fact the last contribution to aviation science made by Martlesham Heath, ably assisted by Woodbridge, and was the culmination of five decades of research and experimentation in the cause of safety in the air.

The Rapid Landing Flight was responsible for investigating the landing

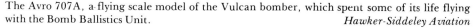

The Avro 707A, a flying scale model of the Vulcan bomber, which spent some of its life flying with the Bomb Ballistics Unit. *Hawker-Siddeley Aviation*

of fighter aircraft at short intervals in bad visibility, a procedure necessary for the efficient operation of Fighter Command. Operating three Gloster Meteor NF.11 two-seat twin-jet fighters, the flight worked in close co-operation with Fighter Command Headquarters. Much of the flying had of necessity to be carried out in the worst weather allowable for flying and in close company with other aircraft, often a dangerous and difficult task. Flight track coverage was by radar. A feature of the unit's work was that the aircraft had always to be ready to operate at any time as the weather dictated, a great strain on both air and ground crews.

In both units a tremendous amount of effort was required to carry out the allotted tasks, as usually only seventeen aircraft were available. Most of them were continually being fitted with all manner of weird and wonderful devices and gadgets, "black boxes" and the like, and strenuous efforts were required from all involved, especially the ground crews, to keep these aircraft airworthy. Visits were made all over the British Isles by the resident Engineering Officer to obtain spares for the motley collection, the only source often being of the "Christmas Tree" variety, taking bits and pieces off unserviceable aircraft at one station in order to keep those at another one flying. Life was not at all easy for the aircrews who daily took these aircraft aloft, as many were non-pressurized making it necessary for oxygen masks to be worn. The work of the aircrews was further hampered by the fact that the majority of the aircraft were unheated, making it necessary for the crews to wear bulky warm clothing which greatly restricted their movement within the aircraft.

As one might expect when such experimental work is being carried out, there were several untoward incidents. On one occasion a Lincoln was forced to jettison its bomb load on a night sortie, the bombs falling on farmland at Sudbourne, causing the death of a cow, and on another occasion a Lincoln released a very large bomb as it came in to land at Martlesham Heath, the bomb slithering along the tarmac between the aircraft's undercarriage legs. Both these incidents are fully described in *Orfordness — Secret Site*.

The work of the experimental flights at Sutton Heath and Martlesham Heath came to an end in May, 1957, when the research operation was transferred to the Royal Aircraft Establishment at Bedford. It was a contribution to aeronautical science which is preserved in the memories of those who took part as well as in the systems today used by airlines the world over.

CHAPTER TEN

The New Company

WITH the end of the war in Europe R.A.F. Woodbridge was put on a care and maintenance basis, with a small staff of maintenance men looking after essential items of service equipment and keeping the buildings and installations in weatherproof condition so that the Station could be made ready in the minimum of time should it be needed again. The only flying that took place was that carried out by the experimental units described in the previous chapter.

This situation was entirely changed on 5th June, 1952, when new uniforms, different vehicles and unfamiliar aircraft were seen at Sutton Heath for the first time. A language which was reminiscent of that heard on many East Anglian airfields during the Second World War was heard as the United States Air Force took over administrative control of the Station.

R.A.F. Woodbridge now became the home base of the 79th Fighter Bomber Squadron, part of the 20th Fighter Bomber Wing, later redesignated the 20th Tactical Fighter Wing, of the U.S.A.F. — the U.S. Army Air Force of the war years had become part of a new service. The unit's object was to prepare for, execute and support offensive air operations against enemy forces, installations and resources, a secondary commitment being to assist in the air defence of the United Kingdom.

Logistical support was obtained from the 81st Fighter Bomber Wing at nearby R.A.F. Bentwaters until in September, 1952, this responsibility passed to the 20th Fighter Bomber Wing's own facility at Wethersfield, in Essex.

The wing was equipped with the Republic F-84E Thunderjet, which was replaced in 1957 by the supersonic North American F-100 Super Sabre fighter bomber. Aircraft of this calibre were new to the strip. Instead of the piston engines of the bombers and their top speeds in the region of 300 m.p.h., the Thunderjet with its Allison J.35 turbojet rated at 5,600 lb. static thrust had a top speed of about 605 m.p.h., a service ceiling of 45,000 feet and, with overload tanks, a combat radius of 1,000 miles. Armament was still the machine-gun, the F-84E carrying six 0.5 inch M.3 guns, although as an alternative load it could carry thirty-two five-inch high-velocity aerial rockets or two 11.5 inch rocket projectiles and sixteen of the five-inch variety. The aircraft weighed in at 11,000 lb. empty and 18,000 lb. loaded.

The Republic F-84F Thunderstreak, with which the 81st Tactical Fighter

169

Wing at Bentwaters and later at Woodbridge was equipped, was a slightly smaller aircraft in wingspan, being three feet less than the F-84E, but it was six feet longer with a Wright J.65 turbojet rated at 7,200 lb. static thrust giving it a top speed of 710 m.p.h. Service ceiling had been raised to 50,000 feet and the maximum range with overload tanks was no less than 2,500 miles. There was also an appreciable increase in all-up weight, which was 25,000 lb. Armament was till six 0.5 inch machine-guns, four mounted in the front fuselage and one in each wing, with twenty-four five-inch H.V.A.R. missiles or four 1,000 lb. bombs.

The Thunderstreaks proved somewhat unlucky aircraft, three of them being lost in two Suffolk incidents. On Tuesday, 6th May, 1955, Captain Walter S. Bruce was on a high-altitude training flight when his Thunderstreak's engine "flamed out"—that is, the flame necessary to ignite the atomised fuel went out—at 35,000 feet. After descending to 6,000 feet, Captain Bruce ejected from the aircraft and landed safely, the aircraft crashing in the village of Boyton, about four miles from the airfield. Exploding as it hit ground, the jet scattered blazing wreckage over a large area, starting several small fires which were quickly put out by Suffolk firemen. Fortunately on this occasion no injuries were suffered by any of the villagers.

A second incident on 23rd May, 1956, proved more tragic in its consequences. Two Thunderstreaks from R.A.F. Wethersfield had been carrying out an air-refuelling exercise north-east of Felixstowe when they touched wingtips. One of them climbed sharply after the collision, turned over and dropped vertically, crashing into an open field at Alderton; the pilot died as the machine exploded on impact.

The pilot of the other Thunderstreak ejected from his aircraft and was picked up, only slightly injured, from Ramsholt Marshes by a helicopter. His aircraft smashed into a cottage outhouse in Main Street, Bawdsey, killing eighty-year-old Mr Isaac Ford, who was working in the building at the time. Mr Ford's forty-nine-year-old son, Mr Edgar Ford, staggered from the inferno and was rushed to hospital in Ipswich; he later made a full recovery from his injuries.

Later in the 1950s a faster and more powerful aircraft, the F-100 Super Sabre, took up residence with the 79th at Woodbridge. Of much the same size as the Thunderstreak, the Super Sabre was powered by a Pratt and Whitney J.57 rated at 9,500 lb. static thrust, with 14,250 lb. available with afterburning. This power made the F-100 supersonic, with a top speed of 1.25 mach (950 m.p.h.) at 45,000 feet and a maximum sea level speed of 750 m.p.h. The operational ceiling was still 50,000 feet, but with the much more thirsty J.57 turbojet the combat radius was only 600 miles. Normal loaded weight was 22,000 lb., but the design allowed operation at an all-up gross weight of

26,000 lb. Armament of the Super Sabre was four 20 mm M.39 cannons in the front fuselage and, as underwing loads, four 750 lb. Napalm tanks, two 2,000 lb. bombs or forty-five 2.75 inch "Mighty Mouse" rocket projectiles. On 5th September, 1955, a specially prepared Super Sabre had established a speed record of 822.174 m.p.h. over the Nevada Desert.

Operational control of R.A.F. Woodbridge was transferred from the 20th Tactical Fighter Wing, as the unit was by then known, to the 81st Tactical Fighter Wing on 8th July, 1958, but the 79th Tactical Fighter Squadron remained at the base until September, 1969, when it began a move to R.A.F. Upper Heyford, in Oxfordshire. Following this change of operational control one of the 81st Wing's squadrons, the 78th Tactical Fighter Squadron, moved from R.A.F. Shepherds Grove, near Stanton in West Suffolk, to Woodbridge in December, 1958, and January, 1959. At the same time the 78th was converting from the F-84F Thunderstreak to the F-101 Voodoo, with which the 81st Wing's two other squadrons were also being equipped.

The first of the new McDonnell F-101A Voodoo twin-engined heavy fighters appeared at the twin bases of Woodbridge and Bentwaters in the first week of December, 1958, having flown the 5,500 miles from Shaw Air Force Base, South Carolina, in ten and a half flying hours, with a stop in Morocco. Twice refuelled in the air on the first leg of their trans-ocean flight, they flew the 1,380 miles from Morocco in one hop.

A Republic F-84F Thunderstreak of the kind with which the 81st Tactical Fighter Wing was equipped.   *U.S.A.F.*

By comparison with earlier American jet fighters the Voodoo was a large aircraft, spanning 39½ feet and measuring 67 feet from nose to tail, with an all-up weight of 50,000 lb. Its two Pratt and Whitney J.57-P.13 turbojets gave it a top speed of 1,009 m.p.h. at 35,000 feet and a ceiling of over 55,000 feet.

Local residents soon grew accustomed to the ear-splitting howl of these new machines. Although they were fitted with afterburners to provide added power on take-off and when in action, stringent restrictions were imposed on the aircrew by Operating Control to limit the amount of noise to a level it was felt would be tolerated by local villagers. On the whole it worked out very well and both sides were always on the best of terms.

Within a few days of the arrival of the 78th Tactical Fighter Squadron at Woodbridge its presence at the base was announced by the erection at the main gate of a large notice board, brilliantly coloured, which proclaimed to passers-by that this was the home of the 78th T.F.S., "The Bushmasters". The name was emphasised by the portrayal of a deadly-looking fully-fanged reptile entwined about the wording. The sister squadrons of the 81st Tactical Fighter Wing at nearby Bentwaters also had their names, the 91st being "The Bluestreaks" and the 92nd "The Avengers".

The 81st Tactical Fighter Wing had come into existence as the 81st Pursuit Group back in 1942, its squadrons then being equipped with the unorthodox and somewhat troublesome Bell P-39 Airacobra. It came to Britain in 1951 as the 81st Fighter-Interceptor Group, its F-86A Sabrejets touching down at R.A.F. Bentwaters and R.A.F. Shepherds Grove in September of that year. The mission and name changed in 1954 to the 81st Fighter Bomber Group, the designation being changed again the following year to 81st Fighter Bomber Wing. By this time the Sabrejets had been changed for F-84 Thunderstreaks.

The year 1958 saw two unfortunate incidents involving aircraft from Woodbridge, the first of them occurring in March when a Lockheed P-80 Shooting Star jet trainer struck high-tension electricity transmission cables spanning the Orwell near the Cliff Quay generating station at Ipswich. The aircraft left part of its structure entangled with the cables, which were slung high above the river so as to clear the masts of shipping using the waterway, but it limped back to Woodbridge and landed safely.

The second, more tragic, incident occurred during the last week of December, 1958, when two North American F-100 Super Sabres took off from the base and climbed out towards Ipswich. Shortly after take-off, when over the River Deben, one of the aircraft suffered a "flame-out" which resulted in total loss of power. The pilot, realising his predicament, ejected from the fighter and landed safely, to be picked up shortly afterwards by a helicopter.

The pilotless aircraft continued to climb until loss of airspeed caused its nose to drop, and gathering speed in a shallow dive it crashed into the office

A North American F-100 Super Sabre of the 20th Tactical Fighter Wing resplendent in unit markings. This aircraft is fitted with large underwing long-range fuel tanks.   *U.S.A.F.*

and buildings of Falcon Caravans alongside the A 12 road at Kesgrave, near Ipswich, exploding in a welter of flame as it impacted. The blast killed a woman working in the office, while an Eastern Electricity Board meter reader who had just entered the building was blasted across the front lawn of the office and into a shallow fish-pond, the water providentially extinguishing his blazing clothing. The Pratt and Whitney J.57 turbojet, breaking free from the airframe, careered onwards towards a nearby house. Mr Fred Ward, who was in his garden, was engulfed by blazing kerosene. He died later in hospital. The site proprietor's wife, Mrs Riches, was in the back garden about to feed some chickens; the blast hurled her through a thick hawthorn hedge, but she escaped with nothing more serious than shock.

Although the crash site has been completely rebuilt Mr Riches still finds bits and pieces of the Super Sabre as they gradually work their way to the surface.

Another change of aircraft equipment occurred during the spring of 1966 when the F-101 Voodoos were replaced by another fighter from the same stable, the McDonnel F-4C Phantom II. This large sophisticated twin-jet monoplane, designed originally for the United States Navy for carrier duties, arrived at the base on 2nd March, 1966.

Weighing in at over 50,000lb when fully loaded and capable of 1,459 m.p.h. at 40,000 feet from the power of its two 17,000lb thrust re-heated General Electric J.79 turbojets, this noisy 38 foot wingspan, 63 feet long aircraft soon made an impression on the neighbourhood. Letters appeared in local newspapers complaining about the noise from the Phantoms as their

Renowned in the Woodbridge area for their noisiness, the McDonnell F-4 Phantom two-seat long-range strike fighter was capable of carrying a very heavy armament load over great distances.   *U.S.A.F.*

approach path often passed over the centre of Ipswich. During periods of low cloud and an easterly wind, the F-4s approached their base from the west and passing over the town with their undercarriages and flaps down, flight at this time being of consequence slow, the time taken to pass over the centre of population was prolonged. With the reverberation of the somewhat harsh crackling jet noise amplified by the low cloud ceiling, the Phantom soon gained for itself a reputation of being the world's noisiest aircraft. However new approach paths were established more to the north of the town and the letters and complaints grew less.

Rated high in the arsenal of available N.A.T.O. aircraft, the F-4C Phantom had offensive capability of being able to range for over 650 miles (1,056 kms) while in ferry conditions with overload tanks it could be positioned 1,750 miles (2,815 km) from its base. Armament was varied and could be made up of Sparrow III and Sidewinder anti-aircraft missiles, air-to-ground rockets or other weapons to a maximum weight of 16,000lb (7,257 kg). An unusual feature of the Phantom inherited from its Navy days was the fact that it was fitted with folding mainplanes and a large arrester hook, the latter giving rise to an ingenious arrester cable system being devised at Bentwaters and Woodbridge to stop runaway aircraft when landing.

Fate struck on 13th September, 1967, when a Phantom F-4C crashed when approaching to land, the two-man crew ejecting safely making use of the aircraft's British-designed ejector seats. They were Captain Joseph T. Kirby and First Lieutenant James B. Pierce. Mr J. A. Bloomfield, of Sutton, saw two aircraft flying together. "They started to turn and then one broke away from the other. It went over on to its back, making a screaming noise, and dived straight into a potato field, one mile south of the Woodbridge runway," where it made a large crater, flames shooting up over 100 feet high as it exploded.

On 10th May, 1969, the Station was opened to the public on the occasion of Armed Forces Day to celebrate the 20th anniversary of the formation of N.A.T.O. Large crowds turned up to see the resident aircraft, the F-4C Phantom II, stated at that time to be "the U.S.A.F.'s fastest, slowest and highest-flying operational jet fighter aircraft." All aspects of the Station were on show and several exhibitions were staged to present to the public the work carried out by the U.S.A.F. in Europe, while visiting aircraft from several

Eager crowds wait to file through the fuselage of a giant Douglas C-124C Globemaster II at an open day.

N.A.T.O. countries took part in the flying display. The visitors included Canadian, German and Dutch Lockheed F-104 Starfighters, Danish North American F-100 Super Sabres, Norwegian Northrop F-5 Tigers and Belgian Republic RF-84s.

Less than a month earlier the 81st T.F.W. had received its first F-4D Phantom, a development of the F-4C with improved avionics designed to increase the accuracy of both its air-to-air gunnery and its air-to-ground weapon delivery. The 78th at Woodbridge converted to the F-4D in 1969 but it was not until late in 1973 that the wing became equipped completely with the new model.

It was later in 1969 that the 79th Tactical Fighter Squadron, still a unit of the 20th Tactical Fighter Wing, moved to Upper Heyford. The 79th began

Left: Ugly but extremely functional, the Sikorsky HH-53 Jolly Green Giant Helicopter is part of the equipment of the 67th Aerospace Rescue and Recovery Squadron.

Opposite: A Lockheed HC-130 Hercules of the 67th A.R.R.S. sits on the apron at Woodbridge ready for its call to duty.   *U.S.A.F.*

moving its personnel and equipment in the latter part of November and while the move was still taking place an advance party from a very different unit, the 67th Aerospace Rescue and Recovery Squadron, arrived from Moron Air Base in Spain. The A.R.R.S. completed its move, made with the object of providing greater rescue coverage in the North Atlantic area, early in 1970.

As the world's largest rescue squadron, it covered an area stretching from the North Pole to the South Pole and from mid-Atlantic to the borders of Burma, an area of approximately 68,000,000 square miles. Within that enormous area it had the primary duty of maintaining a capability of snatching personnel from behind enemy lines, or from wherever it was necessary to rescue them. In this role the squadron is always on constant standby, twenty-four hours a day, 365 days a year.

In addition it also has the primary recovery responsibility for Atlantic and Indian Ocean splash-downs in connection with N.A.S.A. space missions. As new deployment areas were envisaged for future operations, so the 67th's sphere of operations grew.

The primary means of carrying out their missions is by means of the large, well-proven Lockheed HC-130 Hercules four-turbo-prop powered transport, ideal for the tasks involved. With the ability to loiter at low altitudes or dash to the scene of an emergency at high speed and high altitude, the "Herk" is the acknowledged workhorse and is used by the majority of the air forces of the Free World. With a crew of eight, the HC-130 is capable of travelling at a speed of 330 knots (380 m.p.h.) at above 30,000 feet and can carry a load of 36,700lb beyond 4,000 miles. Equipped in its rescue version with specialised search and rescue avionics and air droppable equipment, it is fitted with an air-to-air refuelling system enabling it to refuel its search and rescue stable companion, the HH-53 Jolly Green Giant heavy helicopter, prolonging its useful duration over the search area. For sea rescues the

helicopter is the main component in air lifting rescue work, hovering above a wreck or crash to haul the survivors to safety. Modern advances in instrumentation enable the flight deck crew to see the surface, whatever the weather conditions, on a television display screen, thus overcoming one of the hazards of extremely bad weather operations.

Invaluable for the close-in rescue role, the HH-53 is a twin-turbo-engined single-rotor helicopter, fully equipped for night and day search and rescue operations. Large by any standard, the HH-53 has a five-bladed rotor with a diameter of 72 feet and a fuselage length of 67 feet, the massive rotor and tail rotor being driven by two 3,435-shaft-horse-power General Electric T64-GE-7 engines, and take-off weight can exceed 42,000lb (19,050 kg). Equipment includes air refuelling probe, jettisonable auxiliary fuel tanks and a variety of armament for use in operations in enemy territory. Crew comprises pilot, co-pilot, flight mechanic and two pararescuemen, the latter three also manning the aircraft's three 7.62 mm miniguns when necessary.

One of the most important sections of the squadron is the Pararescue

Section, an elite company of dedicated, highly professional men trained to be capable of operating under any conditions at all times. Woodbridge has the largest Pararescue Unit in the world, and so exclusive are the men who perform this task that there are only 264 of them worldwide. Only that relatively small number are eligible to wear the maroon beret and badge bearing the unit crest which are the visual symbol of their calling.

To counter the dangerous situations that a Pararescue man may find himself in, he must always be at the peak of physical fitness and the training is always hard, demanding and relentless. All the men on the strength are constantly assessed as to their range of skills, and indeed in the examinations one foul mark means that the man is removed from operational duties until that deficiency has been made good. Known as P.J.s for short, they have come to be among the most respected men in the service, and many a grounded and despairing airman or exhaused civilian has been comforted to see the arrival of one of their number. Medical skills are obviously a very important part of the P.J.'s life and simulated emergencies are a feature of the day's work at Woodbridge in order to put the team through their paces. The P.J. must be instantly familiar with all his equipment, and able to use any of it effectively with his eyes closed.

As the 67th A.R.R.S. has such a vast area of operations, the P.J. must be conversant with the use of anti-malaria pills in tropical environments as well as with such skills as ski-ing and ice cliff climbing in sub-zero temperatures.

When the alert is sounded one of the squadron's Lockheed HC-130 Hercules with its flight crew and probably an eight-man Pararescue team will take off from the strip. Using a device which was a spin-off from the Apollo Spaceshots, called the Apollo Beacon, the crew of the "Herk" are eventually able to locate the downed airman by means of his emergency transmitter. Should the mission be directed towards a civilian objective and therefore without the essential transmitter, a lengthy search may result. This is greatly aided by the fitting of massive long-range fuel tanks which enable it to fly on its search mission for up to thirty-six hours. Should the search area be in mid-ocean the search time is somewhat reduced and the "Herk" has to make for another base nearer to its search area instead of returning to home base.

The cost of this type of work is high, the replacement cost of an HH-53 now being in excess of three and a half million pounds, and it is essential that the back-up servicing and maintenance is of the highest order. The aircraft have to be ready at all times to perform any tasks required of them.

Typical of the men of the 67th are Technical Sergeant Brian Berg and Flight Sergeants James O'Brien and Terry Brisher. The first, a giant of a man,

The moment of rescue: a parachute jumper prepares a casualty for lifting into the hovering HH-53. *U.S.A.F.*

is fully qualified as a skier, athlete, parachutist, scuba-diver, navigator, swimmer and medical first-aider. As if that were not enough, he was preparing to be a member of the team which was to attempt a no-oxygen ascent of the west face of Mount Everest. He said:

> "I suppose we are a cross between the Special Air Service, Mountain Rescue and the R.A.F.'s Search and Rescue people. We combine all their qualities but retain as our basic motivation a humanitarian aim — to save lives. We will parachute on to vessels of any nationality to provide medical treatment and know no bounds of political restraint."

To bear this out the 67th, operating from its Icelandic sub-base at Keflavik, often flies out to the aid of Russian trawlers in Northern waters with crewmen on board who need medical aid.

The unit is fully integrated into the local scheme of things and apart from rescue work the HH-53s have been used for special heavy lift work outside their range of military duties. The Leisure Sport Air Museum at Thorpe Park, Surrey, sold an ex-Royal Navy de Havilland Sea Vixen, XP 919, to the Eastern Counties Aircraft Association at Norwich. Unfortunately the aircraft, which is a twin-jet carrier fighter and rather on the heavy side, was in such a position that it could not be lifted by a crane, so the R.A.F. was approached for help.

A Sikorsky HH-53 airlifts a Royal Navy Westland Wessex which had run into trouble.
U.S.A.F.

Fixed-wing and rotary-wing aircraft formate for a fly-past over the Woodbridge base. The HC-130 has its flaps partly lowered in order to maintain position just ahead of the slower helicopters.   *U.S.A.F.*

Operational difficulties at the last moment prevented the R.A.F. Boeing Chinook twin-rotor helicopter from performing the task and an urgent call to the 67th A.R.R.S. resulted in a promise of immediate assistance. A Jolly Green Giant flown by Captain St Romain arrived on 17th August, 1981, to do the job, but it was found that the Sea Vixen was too heavy for a safe lift. After the removal of several of the heavier components, another HH-53, this time flown by Captain Grey, safely carried out the lift on 25th August.

Many commendable rescues have been performed by the 67th A.R.R.S. since they arrived at Woodbridge. An unusual job arose on 10th April, 1975. While flying from Woodbridge to Lyneham, in Wiltshire, the crew of an HC-130 was asked to assist in the search for the pilot of a Hawker Harrier "jump-jet" who had ejected. After an extensive search the HC-130 located the pilot in a wood near Shawbury, Worcestershire, called up a helicopter to the pilot's rescue, directed it to him, and then continued on its way to Lyneham; all part of a day's work.

Earlier, on 2nd April, 1973, an HH-53 participated in the rescue of the crew of the m.v. *Amberley* which was in difficulties fifteen miles off the North

Norfolk coast. Working in co-operation with Westland Whirlwinds of the R.A.F.'s No. 22 Search and Rescue Squadron from Coltishall, Norfolk, the American helicopter helped rescue the sixteen-man crew of the sinking collier. Other "tasks" performed ranged from rescuing climbers, lifting yachtsmen, rescuing military and civilian airmen down in the sea, mercy errands to gas and oil rigs, and dropping feed to cattle cut off by bad weather as far afield as Devon and Cornwall.

More recently on 13th February, 1982, thirteen Woodbridge-based airmen were involved in a rescue mission in the Atlantic that saw seventeen men winched to safety from the battered remains of a Greek tanker. An HC-130 Hercules from Woodbridge had been frustrated in a bid to save the survivors as they clung desperately to the stern of the 12,480 tonne *Victory*, the only part of the ship still afloat. The ship had been torn apart by raging seas. When winds dropped to Force 6 at dawn the Dutch frigate *Van Speyk* launched its British-built Westland Lynx helicopter, which was able to move in and mount a rescue mission which lasted ninety minutes. The HC-130 stayed near the scene all night and throughout the rescue, and was joined by another HC-130 at midday. Both aircraft scanned the area 800 miles off Land's End for survivors in life rafts, but fifteen remained unaccounted for at the end of the operation, the "Herks" working in co-operation with the Falmouth Coastguard Rescue Headquarters. HH-53s were standing by in readiness at Woodbridge should they be required to dash to the disaster scene.

Again during the middle of March, 1982, Woodbridge-based airmen went to the rescue of a sinking Icelandic ship, helping to save the lives of ten men. Major David Hughes and his crew from the 67th Aerospace Rescue and Recovery Squadron joined the search for a lifeboat containing survivors from the foundering ship *Suderland*. The pararescue team, with life rafts ready, led the rescue when an R.A.F. Hercules was forced to turn back through lack of fuel. Two men from the lifeboat had already been rescued by a helicopter from a Danish frigate before all trace of the boat was lost because of bad weather. An R.A.F. Nimrod that arrived to join in the search found the boat and an R.A.F. Sea King helicopter from Lossiemouth picked up the survivors, but the Woodbridge team in the HC-130 was credited with ten lives saved as a result of the operation.

It is comforting to merchant seamen, fishermen and yachtsmen to know that this fine rescue organization is in being and at almost instant readiness should they need the services of the 67th A.R.R.S. Both the dark green HC-130s and the HH-53s are a familiar sight and sound to East Anglians, and are regarded by them as part and parcel of the way of life in this area.

Before the arrival of the HH-53s at Woodbridge a few of the quaint HH-43 Huskies were based there for rescue duties and for quelling airfield crash fires by hovering over the flames and beating them down with the downdraught from their inter-meshing rotors.

When the HC-130s first arrived a few of them were fitted with the Fulton Air-Rescue System by which grounded aircrew could be picked up from the ground using long probes fitted on the aircraft's front fuselage. A rocket pack lifted the airman into the path of the approaching "Herk" and the probes engaged lines to lift the man into the aircraft.

The work of the unit is summed up in the Creed and Motto which reads:

"It is my duty as a member of the AEROSPACE RESCUE AND RECOVERY SERVICE to save life and aid the injured. I will be prepared at all times to perform my assigned duties quickly and efficiently, placing these duties above desires and comforts."

To celebrate the Bicentennial of the United States of America in 1976 and also the twenty-fifth anniversary of the 81st Tactical Fighter Wing's arrival in England the Station held an open day which attracted very large

Right: Visiting American airmen on an exchange visit. The officer in the dark uniform is wearing R.A.F. wings as well as his American wings.

Below: A Dassault Mystere IV of the French Air Force on an exchange visit.

numbers of visitors, who were welcomed by a letter from the Base Commander, Colonel Gerald D. Lanson.

The role of the Station changed somewhat when it was announced during 1978 that the 81st Tactical Fighter Wing was to re-equip with the somewhat unorthodox Fairchild A-10 Thunderbolt II tactical strike fighter, known to its less enthusiastic admirers as "The Warthog". Instead of the powerful roaring concept of the heavy fighter bomber, this was an almost docile-looking aircraft with its parallel chord wing, twin fins and rudders and twin turbojets mounted side by side high on the rear fuselage.

Looks can be misleading as the A-10 is a lethal weapon, designed to combat the severe threat posed by the massive imbalance of ground armour between the Warsaw Pact countries and those of the N.A.T.O. alliance. A single-seat monoplane with short take-off and landing capabilities, an extra-ordinary load carrying capacity and built-in survivability in its low level attack role, the A-10 carries its pilot in a tough titanium armour-plated "bath-tub" cockpit enclosure.

Conspicuous is the protruding 30mm. multi-barrelled Gatling GAU-8A gun system capable of firing at either 2,100 or 4,200 rounds a minute, with a magazine carrying 1,350 rounds. Other stores carried include conventional and laser-guided weapons, rockets, cluster bombs, Maverick missiles and electronic countermeasures equipment to a total weight of 16,000lb. The A-10 is the only close support aircraft capable of diving at steeply controlled angles to deliver its gunfire or stores on to its target. A great relief to the residents of the district under the approach flight-path are the A-10's two General Electric TF.34-100 turbofan engines of 9,000lb thrust, smokeless and quiet as opposed to the F-4's window-shaking powerplants.

Unfortunately the new aircraft suffered a few teething troubles, with one A-10 crashing at R.A.F. Chicksands while giving a display. Two more were involved in a mid-air collision over North Norfolk and another was lost while carrying out armament exercises off the Lincolnshire coast.

These 55 foot wingspan aircraft now take off and land with the larger "Herks" on Woodbridge's massive runway, while the Jolly Green Giants use their dispersal areas for that purpose.

The men of the U.S.A.F. have become so integrated in the Suffolk way of life that preservation of historic vehicles has become part of their activities. The fifty-eight members of the Woodbridge Base Fire Department clubbed together to raise £600 to buy a 1958 Bedford fire tender from a local breaker's yard. The tender, retired by Suffolk County Fire Service late in 1981, was in good mechanical order and has now come under the wing of Master Sergeants Robert Reid and David Osterberg, who plan to have it back, spick and span, ready for open days and, if necessary, as a back-up vehicle for civilian fire crews.

Top: Housing built at Woodbridge for U.S.A.F. personnel.

Right: Woodbridge High School is the centre of learning for teenage American students during their parents' overseas posting.

Below: Some U.S.A.F. families live in these "fourplex units" adjacent to the base chapel.

M/Sgt Vickie Graham, U.S.A.F.

185

Demonstrators appeared on the scene at Easter, 1982, when members of the East Anglia Campaign For Nuclear Disarmament released balloons from selected sites in East Anglia. Woodbridge was on the list and altogether 106 balloons were released, to equal the number of nuclear weapons supposedly dropped on Britain during the Government's "Square Leg" civil defence exercise in 1979. The Peace Week ended with a demonstration march on Saturday, 10th April, 1982, when the column walked from the gates of R.A.F. Woodbridge to Ipswich, there they were addressed by members of the

Fairchild A-10 Thunderbolt IIs of the 81st Tactical Fighter Wing which share the Woodbridge base with the aircraft of the 67th A.R.R.S.   *U.S.A.F.*

movement and local dignitaries, including the leader of Ipswich Borough Council, Mr Jamie Cann, and the Bishop of Dunwich, the Right Reverend Eric Davenport.

In spite of such protests R.A.F. Woodbridge remains in full commission, but the runway is now much smaller than it once was, the sides have grown over and the length has decreased dramatically. Gone is the F.I.D.O., no longer needed with the advent of modern navigational aids; gone is the massive fuel dump to supply the needs of the thirsty fog-dispelling F.I.D.O.; gone are all the bulldozers, cranes and crash gear, the heaps of wreckage and crazily twisted aircraft; and gone even is the station at Melton from which so many wrecked aircraft made their last journey to the smelter's pot. Gone are the bell tents from among the fir-trees and the Nissen huts around the dispersal loops, and risen in their stead are modern houses for the married families, a fine new hospital, an equally elegant High School for the children attached to the base, and many other facilities unthought of during the days of the "Crash 'Drome".

186

CHAPTER ELEVEN

The Quilters of Bawdsey Manor

ALTHOUGH born in 1841 in the City of London, Cuthbert Quilter was closely connected with East Suffolk as he was the grandson of a Trimley gentleman with a large farm, Mr Samuel Quilter. While on a holiday at his grandfather's farm at Trimley he got a lift on a farmer's cart which was on its way to the hamlet of Felixstowe Ferry. On arrival he sat and contemplated the headland which jutted out to sea on the other side of the Deben's mouth. The scene evoked the thought in his youthful mind that if one day, like his illustrious forebear, Sir Richard Whittington, he made his fortune he would return to that spot across the river and there build his home.

In due course his ambitions were realised. After working diligently, he progressed in the stockbroking firm of Quilter, Balfour and Company and eventually became its head official and also a member of the Stock Exchange, where he conducted dealings at an international level. Until 1873 he had resided in Surrey, where he was the Commanding Officer of the 4th Surrey Rifles, a local volunteer army unit, but in that year he moved to Suffolk, where at the age of thirty-two he started to build his new home, to be named Bawdsey Manor. In order to do so he moved the main road, which ran across the land on which he sited his house.

Taking some nine years to complete in its early form, the large building on its windswept promontory overlooking the often grey North Sea did not project any one period of architecture, but ranged from the style of the English Elizabethan house to that of an Eastern potentate's palace. Quilter appeared well pleased with his new acquisition but was never quite satisfied with the final structure. It is reputed that as his fortunes grew, so did the Manor, and that as each million-pound mark was passed, so another tower was added, there being nine such additions at the final count.

Quilter's next step was a logical one. Like all good country gentlemen he stood for Parliament, becoming the Member for South Suffolk during 1885. His performance in the House was not outstanding but he was greatly liked in his constituency, one of his more prominent Parliamentary campaigns being to promote a "Pure Beer Bill". To support this idea he opened a small brewery in the main street of Melton, a village on the upper tidal reaches of the Deben next to Woodbridge. This establishment produced pure beer for only a short time, closing down quite soon.

Quilter's progress in the Liberal Party was not marked by great fame due to his often bitter and pointed criticism of his leader's aims, and in particular of Mr Gladstone's policy of Home Rule. Nevertheless, in spite of refusing a knighthood on three occasions, during 1906 he was created a Baronet after losing his seat by a slender 136 votes during the Elections held earlier in that year.

The golden era was slowly drawing to a close as new tax laws, aimed at carving a larger slice of income from the large country landowners, hit hard, and Sir Cuthbert suffered with the rest. He complained bitterly, voicing his annoyance and anger at the situation. In the end a vast picture collection which he had inherited from his father, and which hung at his London house, No. 28 South Street, Park Lane, went under the hammer, being auctioned by Christies for £87,780 in July, 1909. The income from this sale eased the situation for a while, but Sir Cuthbert still expressed the view that large estates up and down the country were being bled dry by an unrelenting sequence of governments.

One thing that his estate was not short of was land, as it ran to some 8,000 acres, stretching almost the whole way along the north bank of the River Deben from Bawdsey to Melton. Self administered, the estate had its own offices at Bawdsey, and it was here that skilled craftsmen such as wheelwrights, blacksmiths and builders had their workshops to cope with all the requirements of the Manor and its farms.

The major part of the estate was wild heathland, covered with heather, gorse, bracken and stunted pine trees which ran in long stretches over the flat heaths. On the more hospitable grounds, considerable farming was carried out and at Bawdsey Hall, just up the road from the Manor, a stud of Suffolk horses was gradually built up; many prizes came their way, both from local and distant shows. Sir Cuthbert's flock of Suffolk sheep which cropped the short salty grasses gained equal recognition at the shows.

The estate's forestry section carried out a carefully planned nursery and replanting scheme, so that as the more mature timber was felled it was replaced by new stock. These saplings also provided stock for planting the many windbreaks which were positioned to protect the farmed lands with their light soil from the strong winds which tended to "blow off" both soil and seed in great clouds of blinding dust during times of drought, no rare occurrence in this area.

Quilter took the task of looking after the estate very seriously and had the welfare of his employees close to his heart. He was the first landlord in the district to erect up-to-date houses for the estate workers. Many stories live on of his acts of kindness to the local population, such as when he inaugurated a scheme to alleviate unemployment by causing his sandpits to be worked for flints for road making.

On the other hand, after a fire had occurred on one of the farms, a blaze which had started in very suspicious circumstances, Quilter investigated it assiduously; and on visiting the farmer a few days later told him that if he looked in the shaving mirror he would see the person responsible for starting the blaze! His seemingly good nature could be clouded when confronted with misdemeanours by the local people and poaching was to the Squire an unforgivable sin. Any man brought before him for this offence could expect no mercy and would find it almost impossible to obtain further employment in the district.

Life at the Manor was not exactly a bed of roses as the Head of the Manor maintained strict discipline. None of the household was allowed to speak without first being addressed by the Squire. This applied to all members of the family as well as to the servants, but one resident who would not accept this

Ferry Cottages on the Bawdsey shore with the Main Gate to R.A.F. Bawdsey on the extreme left.
T. N. Briggs

ruling was the local Vicar, the Reverend Allott Tighe-Gregory, incumbent of the living of All Saints, Bawdsey, from 1848 until 1911. He was a continual thorn in the flesh of the Squire and resisted all attempts by Sir Cuthbert to unseat him. Quilter even instructed the tenants to attend Bawdsey Manor Chapel, in the Manor grounds, instead of the village church, and built a second school in the village, demanding that all the children attend it instead of the Church School.

The fact that Sir Cuthbert, who served as Commodore of the Royal Harwich Yacht Club from 1879 to 1909, loved the sea, did not stop the North Sea from whittling away at the south side of the estate, close to the Manor itself. Dutch engineers were called in to construct sea defences at a cost of £120,000, but to no avail.

The Squire expanded his realm and the purchase of Laurel Farm, Felixstowe, on the south bank of the River Deben, gave rise to another Quilter enterprise, the installation of a steam chain ferry across the river mouth. Two steam-powered, double-ended vehicular ferries were employed, one named *Lady Quilter*, and these two vessels plied the ferry route for some years. Business was brisk in the early days but gradually fell away and eventually, due

to increasing losses, the ferry ceased running during the 1920's. For many years the two ferries lay rusting and forgotten in the little dock on the Bawdsey side of the river but they were eventually sold for scrap and broken up.

Another enterprise which did not get off the ground was Quilter's attempt to popularise the village of Bawdsey as a fashionable seaside resort, much as George Tomline had already done at Felixstowe. This as far as Bawdsey was concerned did not get past the planning stage, and Bawdsey-on-Sea lived only as a pipe and paper dream.

Sir Cuthbert collapsed and died in 1911 at the age of 70, mourned by all the villagers and especially those on the Manor estate, who were all provided for in his will. The Manor passed to the hands of his eldest son, Sir W. Cuthbert Quilter (born 1873, died 1952). Another son, Roger (born 1877, died 1953), was the noted composer and musician.

The new Squire carried on the welfare work started by his father, but depressions both commercial and agricultural began to undermine the family's finances. Repairs to the sea defences cost more year by year, while rents from the farmers did not cover the expenditure needed for the upkeep of the farms, and eventually heavy death duties made necessary the ultimate sacrifice of Bawdsey Manor. It was sold to the Air Ministry during 1936.

The old squire's grandson, Sir Raymond Quilter (1902-1959), took up residence in the former chauffeur's cottage at Methersgate Hall, on the estate, after inheriting the title from his elder brother. From the same mould as his

Opposite: The steam chain ferry approaches the Felixstowe shore, the Manor in the background standing out above the half-grown conifers.
Mr Richard Crier

Right: The Manor looks out across its lawns like a fairy-tale castle. *Mrs Sylvia Evans*

grandfather, Sir Raymond was a merchant venturer and formed the C.Q. Parachute Company at Woking, Surrey. This form of lifesaving apparatus had always been dear to his heart and he had often given demonstration parachute jumps over Felixstowe seafront, dropping from his own aircraft which he kept on a small landing strip on Sutton Walks.

The scourge of the modern estate manifested itself after the death of Sir Raymond and an announcement in the local paper stated that about 3,160 acres of the family properties would be sold in Ipswich. Over 1,000 acres, two farms, accommodation land, marsh and woodland and the *Ramsholt Arms* would be offered for vacant possession.

The Bawdsey estate had the reputation of being one of the finest game shoots in East Anglia and the level of estate management of this vast area of the Sandlings was an example to all engaged in this task.

Glossary

A.A.	Anti-Aircraft.
A.A.S.	Army Acoustic Section.
A. & A.E.E.	Aeroplane and Armament Experimental Establishment.
A.D.G.B.	Air Defence of Great Britain.
Aerial.	Wire or rod capable of radiating or receiving electromagnetic waves.
A.I.	Air Interception (Radar).
A.I.E.U.	Armament and Instrument Experimental Unit.
Air Estimates.	Money allocated by Government for R.A.F. expenditure.
Aldis Lamp.	Powerful lamp used for signalling.
A.M.	Air Ministry.
A.M.E.S.	Air Ministry Experimental Station.
A.M.W.D.	Air Ministry Works Directorate.
A.O.C.	Air Officer Commanding.
Appleton Layer.	Ionised layer of upper atmosphere which acts as a reflector for radio waves.
A.S.A.	Low level narrow beam radar.
A.S.R.	Air Sea Rescue.
A.S.V.	Air to Surface Vessel (Radar).
Auto transformer.	Transformer with single winding and one tapping.
A.W.D.S.	All Weather Development Squadron.
B.A.B.S.	Blind Approach Beacon System.
Band, Radio.	Radio Frequency.
B.B.U.	Bomb Ballistics Unit.
Black Box.	Term for enclosed electrical device, usually secret; use of this term for a flight recorder fitted to an aircraft is relatively recent.
B.L.E.U.	Blind Landing Experimental Unit.
Blip.	A spot of light on a radar screen indicating an object.
Bod.	R.A.F. term for men (bodies).
Boffin.	General term for scientist.
Bosun's Chair.	Cradle for working over a ship's side or up a mast—also used for work on aerial towers.
B.R.S.	Bawdsey Research Station.
Calvert Bar Lighting.	System of lighting bars leading in to runway approach.
Cathode Ray Tube.	Electronic tube in which a narrow beam of electrons, emitted from an electronic gun, impinges on a fluorescent screen.
C.H.	Chain Home Radio Location/Radar.
Chaff.	American name for "Window".
Chain.	Number of radio stations which co-operate.
C.H.E.L.	Chain Home Extra Low Radio Location/Radar.
C.H.L.	Chain Home Low Radio Location/Radar.
Christmas Tree.	Aircraft gradually being stripped for spares, also known as a Hangar Queen.

Clutter.	Snowing effect on radar screens.
C.O.	Commanding Officer.
Contact light.	Special type of runway light.
C.P.O.	Chief Petty Officer (Royal Navy).
Co-axial cable.	Transmission line comprising an insulated central conductor surrounded by an insulated conducting tube.
C.R.C.	Central Reporting Centre.
C.R.D.F.	Close Range Direction Finder.
C.S.E.	Central Signals Establishment.
C.T.O.	Chief Technical Officer.
Dambuster.	General term used in connection with raid on Ruhr dams in Germany.
Darkie.	Night flying navigational system using radio signals.
D-Day.	Day Allied Forces invaded Europe, 6th June, 1944.
D.F.M.	Distinguished Flying Medal.
Drem Lighting.	Runway outer and approach lighting system.
Dipole.	An antenna comprising a straight conductor of overall length one half wavelength or less with connectors at the centre.
Direction Finder.	Directional receiver for ascertaining maximum and minimum signal response to determine arrival direction of incoming signal.
Down time.	Time spent on maintenance or repairs.
D.R.O.	Daily Routine Orders.
Duppel.	German name for "Window".
Echo.	Returned signal from original transmitted one.
E.C.M.	Electronic Countermeasures.
Ekco.	Trade name for E. K. Cole Limited, radio manufacturers.
E.L.G.	Emergency Landing Ground.
E.M.I.	Electrical Musical Industries, radio manufacturers.
Estuary Chain.	Radio location stations around the Thames Estuary and South-east England.
E.W.S.	Early Warning Station.
F-Layer.	Another name for Appleton Layer in upper atmosphere.
F.I.D.O.	Fog Investigation and Dispersal Organisation.
Flak.	German anti-aircraft gunfire.
Forestry Commission.	Government body responsible for forestry.
Frequency.	The frequency at which an electric current alternates.
Gas Cape.	Anti-gas protective clothing.
G.C.A.	Ground Controlled Approach, by which aircraft is guided in to runway.
G.C.I.	Ground Controlled Interception, used to vector aircraft on to target.
G.E.C.	General Electric Company, electrical manufacturers.
Gee.	Medium range bombing aid using ground transmitters and airborne receivers.
G.L.	Gun Laying (Radar).

GLOSSARY

Goniometer.	A device used for comparison of signal amplitudes.
G.P.O.	General Post Office.
Grand Slam.	22,000lb bomb used on special targets by the R.A.F.
Ground Loop.	Uncontrollable violent swerve by aircraft taking-off or landing.
G.R.S.S.	Ground Radar Servicing Squadron.
H2S.	Airborne centimetric radar used as navigational and bombing aid.
Hardstanding.	Dispersal area for aircraft.
Heaviside Layer.	An ionised region in the upper atmosphere which reflects radio waves.
Hertz.	Unit of frequency, one cycle per second.
H.M.C.	His/Her Majesty's Coastguard.
H.T.	High Tension.
I.F.F.	Identification, Friend or Foe, carried by all R.A.F. and U.S.A.A.F. aircraft.
I.L.S.	Instrument Landing System.
Impedance.	Resistance to current of an alternating current circuit.
Interference.	Any signal, transmitted or atmospheric, other than that which it is intended a receiver should receive.
Jostle.	Jamming device directed at enemy night fighters.
KG.	Kampfgeschwader, Luftwaffe bomber unit consisting of three or four Gruppe plus a Stab (Staff flight).
Km.	Kilometre.
Kw.	Kilowatt.
L.A.C.W.	Leading Aircraftwoman.
Land line.	Direct wire link between two communication centres.
L.D.V.	Local Defence Volunteers, later Home Guard.
L.N.E.R.	London and North Eastern Railway.
Loran.	Hyperbolic navigation system with range of a few thousand miles using frequencies of about 2M/cs and double ground stations.
Lorenz.	German-designed blind landing system.
Luftflotte.	Luftwaffe information, literally translated air fleet.
M.A.E.E.	Marine Aircraft Experimental Establishment.
Magnetron.	Device for generating very high frequency oscillations.
Mandrel.	Airborne radar jamming device.
M.A.P.	Ministry of Aircraft Production.
Martello Tower.	Coastal defence structure erected during the Napoleonic era.
Mayday.	Radio telephony distress signal.
M.B.	Mobile Base.
Mhz.	Megahertz.
Modulation.	Variation of the frequency phase or magnitude of H.F. current.
Monica.	Rearward warning radar carried by R.A.F. bombers.
M.O.S.	Ministry of Supply.

M.R.L.U.	Mobile Radio Location Unit.
M.T.	Motor Transport.
M.T.B.	Motor Torpedo Boat.
Mufti.	Civilian clothing as opposed to uniform.
N.A.S.A.	National Aeronautics and Space Administration (U.S.A.).
N.A.T.O.	North Atlantic Treaty Organisation.
N.C.O.	Non-Commissioned Officer.
N.F.S.	National Fire Service.
N.P.L.	National Physical Laboratory.
O.B.E.	Order of the British Empire.
Oboe.	Ground controlled blind bombing radar system. More accurate than Gee.
Orderly Room.	R.A.F. Station administration office.
Overshoot.	Failure to land within the intended area due to excessive speed or height.
P.F.F.	Pathfinder Force.
Piperack.	Rearward warning radar installed in R.A.F. bombers.
P.P.I.	Plan Position Indicator.
P.S.I.	President of the Service Institute.
Pulse.	A signal of very short duration.
Queen Mary.	R.A.F. lorry for carrying aircraft, usually 60 feet long.
Q.O.	Quarterly Overhaul.
Q-Site.	Dummy airfield with lights.
Radar.	System of locating distant objects by radio transmission on finite and known velocity of propagation of radio waves.
Radio Location.	Early name for radar.
R.A.E.	Royal Aircraft Establishment.
R.A.F.	Royal Air Force.
R.A.F.O.	Reserve of Air Force officers.
R.D.F.	Radio Direction Finding.
Rebecca Eureka.	Set used by airborne forces to direct themselves to established radar beacon.
Receiver.	Equipment which receives signals in electrical form and converts them into desired form.
R.E.M.E.	Royal Electrical Mechanical Engineers.
R.F.	Radio frequency.
R.F.C.	Royal Flying Corps.
R.L.F.	Rapid Landing Flight.
R.N.A.S.	Royal Naval Air Service.
R.N.V.R.	Royal Naval Volunteer Reserve.
R.O.C.	Royal Observer Corp.
R.R.B.	Radio Research Board.
R.R.S.	Radio Research School.
R.R.U.	Radar Reporting Unit.
R/T.	Radio Telegraphy.
Rx.	Receiver.

GLOSSARY

Scrambler.	Telephone security device allowing person-to-person direct speech.
Signal to Noise Ratio.	Decibels by which reproduced speech must be attenuated before it becomes unintelligible because of noise level.
S.O.E.	Special Operations Executive.
Special Duties Flight (D Flt).	Unit based at Martlesham Heath pre-war to provide aircraft for radio location airborne duties.
S.R.S.	Stanmore Research Station.
Staffel.	Luftwaffe formation, with three or four Staffeln of nine to sixteen aircraft each to a Gruppe.
Strip.	Slang word for runway or landing ground.
Strobe.	Enlargement of a part of a waveform as shown on the screen of a cathode ray tube.
Tacon.	Tactical air navigation system.
Tannoy.	General term for public address system; name comes from a manufacturer of public address equipment.
Track.	Projection of flight path upon the earth's surface.
Transformer.	Equipment to convert electrical energy received into different voltage for delivery.
Transmitter.	Apparatus for production and modulation of radio frequency current.
T.R.E.	Telecommunications Research Establishment.
Tx.	Transmitter.
Undershoot.	Failure to reach the intended landing area due to insufficient height or speed.
U.S.A.F.	United States Air Force.
U.S.A.A.F.	United States Army Air Force Force.
V1.	German pilotless flying bomb.
V2.	German long-range rocket.
Very light.	Coloured flare fired from pistol for signalling purposes.
Voltage.	The value of an electromagnetic force or potential difference expressed in volts.
W.A.A.F.	Women's Auxiliary Air Force.
Watch.	Period of duty.
Wattage.	Unit of electrical power (l.H.P. = 746 watts).
Waveguide.	Hollow metal conductor within which very high frequency energy can be transmitted efficiently.
Wavelength.	Distance between two similar and successive points on an alternating wave.
"Window".	Metallised paper strips dropped from aircraft to jam radar reception.
Write-off.	Aircraft damaged beyond repair.
W/T.	Wireless Telegraphy.
Y.M.C.A.	Young Men's Christian Association.

Commanding Officers.

ROYAL AIR FORCE BAWDSEY

25th October, 1939.	Sqdn.Ldr. J. A. Tester.
6th April, 1940.	Sqdn.Ldr. W. Kidd.
12th June, 1940.	Flt.Lt. J. R. Turnbull.
3rd February, 1941.	Flt.Lt. E. Swinney.
31st October, 1941.	Flt.Lt. H. W. Northover.
1st May, 1942.	Sqdn.Ldr. A. M. Hardie.
1st July, 1943.	Sqdn.Ldr. J. R. Wardrop.
6th November, 1944.	Sqdn.Ldr. E. R. Bullimore.
13th June, 1945.	Sqdn.Ldr. C. L. Monk.
February, 1947.	Sqdn.Ldr. S. Colquhoun.
1st December, 1947.	Sqdn.Ldr. A. D. Jackson.
18th August, 1948.	Sqdn.Ldr. K. A. Mummery.

No. 144 SIGNALS UNIT

19th October, 1950.	Sqdn.Ldr. A. R. Gilding.
15th September, 1952.	Sqdn.Ldr. J. A. Theophilus, O.B.E.
14th April, 1954.	Wg.Cmdr. E. P. Wells, D.S.O., D.F.C.
7th August, 1956.	Wg.Cdmr. D. L. Norris-Smith.
1st May, 1958.	Gp.Capt. J. Wallace, D.S.O., D.F.C., A.F.C.

ROYAL AIR FORCE BAWDSEY

18th April, 1960.	Gp.Capt. L. H. Bartlett, D.S.O.
6th May, 1963.	Gp.Capt. J. A. Brignell, O.B.E., D.F.C., M.A., A.F.R.Ae.S.
29th June, 1964.	Wg.Cmdr. H. R. Barrand.
19th October, 1964.	Wg.Cmdr. J. C. Inkson.
6th June, 1966.	Wg.Cmdr. A. Y. Mason, D.F.C.
11th July, 1966.	Gp.Capt. R. E. Gardiner, D.F.C.
14th March, 1969.	Gp.Capt. F. W. Sledmere, A.F.C.
28th January, 1972.	Gp.Capt. D. J. Rhodes, A.F.M.
13th June, 1974.	Wg.Cmdr. E. R. Lacey, D.S.O., O.B.E.
30th July, 1979.	Sqdn.Ldr. A. German.
19th October, 1981.	Sqdn.Ldr. C. I. Dorman-Jackson.

ROYAL AIR FORCE WOODBRIDGE

15th November, 1943.	Wg.Cmdr. D. E. Burnside, D.F.C.
October, 1944.	Wg.Cmdr. P. J. McGlin, D.F.C.

R.A.F. Station Woodbridge

Emergency Landings made at Woodbridge July 1943 to November 1946

Year	Month	Landings		Damaged by Enemy Action	Technical Trouble	Shortage of Fuel	Weather Diversion	Lost Escort Diversion
		Day	Night					
1943	July	9	—	—	1	8	—	—
	August	4	—	—	—	4	—	—
	September	—	—	—	—	—	—	—
	October	2	—	—	1	1	—	—
	November	14	15	6	8	9	3	3
	December	27	16	8	11	23	1	—
Total for 1943		56	31	14	21	45	4	3
1944	January	48	8	7	16	21	11	1
	February	51	17	8	21	35	3	1
	March	93	35	16	46	66	—	—
	April	109	50	32	60	50	—	17
	May	73	37	35	25	44	3	3
	June	89	58	49	32	39	23	4
	July	145	46	44	56	37	45	9
	August	139	48	50	60	27	31	3
	September	200	59	129	43	41	42	4
	October	166	140	91	96	76	40	3
	November	350	108	126	58	96	175	3
	December	363	169	78	90	85	262	17
Total for 1944		1826	775	675	609	617	635	65
1945	January	410	144	18	128	28	377	3
	February	277	99	22	120	104	119	11
	March	130	48	24	103	33	14	4
	April	113	46	16	84	48	9	2
	May	35	12	1	29	4	12	1
	June	18	6	—	22	2	—	—
	July	21	—	—	21	—	—	—
	August	32	—	—	27	1	4	—
	September	29	—	—	28	1	—	—
	October	67	—	—	30	1	36	—
	November	23	3	—	13	—	13	—
	December	7	11	—	8	—	10	—
Total for 1945		1162	369	81	613	222	594	21

1946								
	January	14	8	—	5	2	13	2
	February	9	—	—	1	1	6	1
	March	3	—	—	2	—	1	—
	April	2	—	—	2	—	—	—
	May	2	—	—	2	—	—	—
	June	4	—	—	4	—	—	—
	July	4	—	—	4	—	—	—
	August	—	—	—	—	—	—	—
	September	1	—	—	1	—	—	—
	October	3	—	—	3	—	—	—
	November	1	—	—	1	—	—	—
Totals for 1946		43	8	—	25	5	20	3
Grand Total		3087	1183	770	1268	887	1253	92

Total Landings — 4270

Many emergency landings were made at Sutton Heath by Consolidated B-24 Liberators, though this Suffolk-based B-24 is seen touching down safely at its home base at Metfield. *U.S.A.F.*

General Index

Illustrations in bold type.

Ranks shown are those relevant at the time of the event.

Index of Aeroplanes and Airships

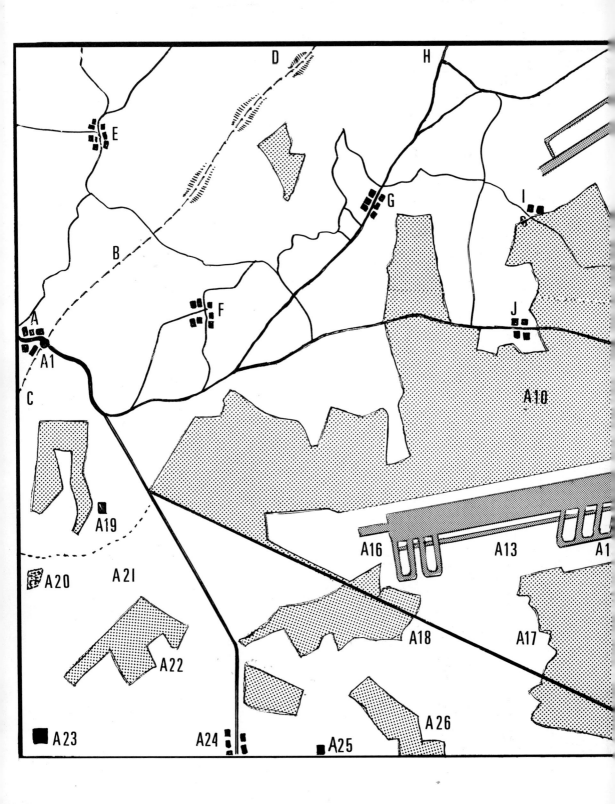